Explorer's Odyssey:
Up a Spiritual Creek
Without a Paddle

An Allegorical Tale About
A Powerful Way to Navigate Through Life

Explorer's Odyssey:
Up a Spiritual Creek
Without a Paddle

An Allegorical Tale About
a Powerful Way to Navigate Through Life

by
Mary Hughes Allen, M.D.

I dedicate this book
with love to my husband,
Donald Phillip Allen,
my helpmate and editor,
the father of my children
whose Jewish tradition
enriched my own mystical
Christian path.

Foreword

I feel honored to be invited to contribute a Foreword for this book. I have known its author for over thirty years, and have watched her persevere in evolving a radical approach to spiritually focused psychotherapy, notwithstanding the skepticism and hostility of many of her colleagues. I have watched her face life-threatening illness as she seemed to experience remission, and later as the disease returned. I have watched her persistently stay alive, seemingly through sheer willpower, to finish this manuscript and see it into production. I would like my Foreword to be a tribute to her determination, her courage, and her spirit.

Explorer's Odyssey is a *Pilgrim's Progress* in a modern idiom. Its psychotherapy is radical in two senses. It is radical because it invites the seeker to take full responsibility for his or her own therapeutic and spiritual progress; it leaves little room for shifting responsibility to childhood environment or therapist. It is also radical because its goal is not just problem solving and psychic comfort, but the fullest possible spiritual enlightenment of the individual human being. This goal is to be pursued despite the disincentives inherent in modern culture, which largely subscribes to more materialistic aims.

I believe I need to say a little more about that. For hundreds of years there has existed a discontinuity between science and the human spirit. A few generations ago this tended to be spoken of as "the conflict between science and religion." By mid-century the conflict was, in some quarters at least, assumed to be over. Science had won, hands down. Whatever "spiritual experience" may be, it was to be explained (or explained away) by an ever more recondite and self-confident science.

Western science has given us our contemporary myths which so strongly influence how we interpret our life experiences. Two of the most powerful of these myths are (1) that the essential characteristics of human nature are to be understood as the consequence of an evolutionary succession of random physical events (from the origin of life to later mutations) and natural selections, and hence are accidental—without purpose or meaning; and (2) that hence the essence of ourselves is to be found in the DNA with which we were born, and any concept resembling the old-fashioned "soul" is pre-scientific superstition. These two myths infuse our education, health care policy, legal justice system, and other social institutions. If they are found to be fundamentally in error, the implications are far-reaching.

For example, if indeed humans fundamentally evolved by mechanistic processes out of a material universe, and if life is basically a set of very complex physical and chemical processes regulated by coded messages in the DNA, then when those processes stop we die, and that is the end of us as physical organisms. If our consciousness, our cherished understandings and values, our individuality, our personhood, are simply creations of those processes, then when those processes stop we are no more. Little wonder that modern society is pervaded by a fear of death, manifesting in multifold subtle ways.

But every satisfactory philosophy of life has disagreed—has asserted that we are in an essentially meaningful universe in which every aspect of life is profoundly meaningful, and the death of the physical body is but a prelude to something else. The mystical and contemplative traditions have often gone on to give more detail with regard to that fundamental meaning, and the nature of our after-death continuation, although probably the insights of these traditions are quite inadequately conveyed by any verbal description.

Our concepts of human development, and our psychotherapies, have been strongly influenced by this tension between the modern scientifically-based myths and our deep spiritual yearnings, and have tended to weigh in on the side of the former. However, particularly since the 1960s, people have increasingly questioned the ability of

Western science—in anything like its present form—to controvert the reality of spirit.

The chief reason to suspect that these modern myths may be in error is that in the exclusion from science of any concept of consciousness as causal (by a choice which started as a division of territory between an upstart science and the powerful Church, and gradually, over a couple of centuries, hardened into an ontological assumption), a fundamental bias was introduced into Western science which is far more basic than the "Newtonian" bias that has been getting such a bad press. That exclusion forces the biologists to seek mechanistic explanations, even in situations where they seem obviously inadequate. (A typical example is the insistence that all the information and motive force to guide ontogeny from fertilized egg to adult organism must reside in some "program" in the DNA.) That exclusion even forced the psychologists, during the "behaviorist era" around mid-century, to deny the reality of the very psyche they presumably were studying.

The late Nobel laureate neuroscientist, Roger Sperry, had long insisted that the scientific account of the universe cannot be complete or accurate unless it includes consciousness as a *causal reality*. But to include consciousness as a causal factor—even though we take that assumption to be obvious in our everyday lives—is to abandon the whole idea of a strictly nomothetic science, a scientific worldview within which everything obeys inviolable "scientific laws" and conscious intention has no place. The quantified relationships of conventional science do, of course, describe what happens under those conditions when consciousness as a causal factor is not interfering; and so they continue to be useful for prediction, control, and the design of manipulative technologies. But that science—quantum physics and chaos theory included—*is in no way qualified to affirm or deny the efficacy of consciousness, nor to deny meaningfulness to spiritual experience.*

The contemporary sociologist and philosopher, Ken Wilber, in his recent writings offers a useful way of thinking about this situation. He notes that the worldviews of practically all societies, with the exception of Western modern, have agreed in certain core characteristics. A central understanding of this "perennial wisdom" is that the world of material things is somehow embedded in a *living* universe, which in turn is within a realm of consciousness, or Spirit. Things are not—cannot be—separate; everything is a part of this "great chain of being."

In this representation of reality one finds a continuum from matter to Spirit (or, if you wish, "levels": matter-body-mind-soul-Spirit). The perennial wisdom claims that the human being can potentially be directly, noetically aware of all levels, from matter to Spirit. Western science chose to focus on the matter end of the continuum, and on up*ward* causation only. In this single fact lie both the power (basically, to create manipulative technology) and the limitation of its epistemology. This restriction of science to only a portion of "the great chain of being" was useful and justifiable for a particular period in history. The only mistake made was to become so impressed with the powers of prediction-and-control science that we were tempted to believe that kind of science could lead us to an understanding of the whole.

What must be done now, in this picture, is to retain the open-minded scientific spirit, and the tradition of open, public validation of knowledge (that is, abjuration of a scientific priesthood), and to open up the field of inquiry to the entire continuum from matter to Spirit, and to downward as well as upward causation. Whether that will be soon done within science is an open question. But if it is not, and people are increasingly persuaded by a philosophy compatible with the "perennial wisdom," the legitimacy of science's claim to be the *only* generally recognized cognitive authority in the modern world will inevitably be brought into question.

In the case of the therapeutic arts, this discontinuity between spirit and the scientifically-real world continues to be present. The cutting edge of this schism today can be seen in the fact that in the development of the new powerful tool of Cognitive Therapy, the dimension of spirituality has been totally excluded. Yet these spiritual realms are crucial to our learning to manage the driving forces in our inner experiences.

These driving forces are the most powerful untamed energies we know. At the time when there was widespread fear of an imminent nuclear holocaust, it was not the nuclear energy that was untamed; rather, it was the energies in the psyches of human beings who might initiate the explosions. As we look around us with clear eyes and see the progressive degradation of our natural environment, and recognize that the trends of modern society are not remotely sustainable on the planet in the long term, the problem is not one of physical pollutants and runaway technologies; it is a problem of the collective psyche and the shared unconscious assumptions of the modern world.

The place to start taming these forces is in the laboratory of the inner experience of each one of us. Everyone has, from time to time, felt inner distress (fear, dread, anger, sadness, what the author calls "agitated energies"); the confusion and muddle over the meaning of life; and the exhaustion and depression from wrestling with these experiences. The many great books of the world which offer guidance in these matters, seem to write in confusing paradoxes: On one page, they suggest a solution (such as to take up arms and fight the evil) and on another page they advocate what seems to be just the opposite (relax, be loving, meditate, and pray). What can we cling to that is stable, always true, and always works best? How can we know what we are doing as we navigate this sea of paradoxes that we call life? How can we calm the agitation and control overwhelming feelings and at the same time find the energy to give our lives meaning and purpose?

Explorer's Odyssey: Up a Spiritual Creek Without a Paddle helps us find our own answers to those questions. It is unique, in expanding the powerful tools of cognitive psychology into the realm of spiritual energies, thus offering a stable, workable frame of reference for both generating and taming the inner forces. In easy-to-read allegorical form it presents fictional characters encountering generic problems, and invites self-discovery of new insight in a coherent step-by-step manner. I feel confident that both individual seeker and practicing therapist will find it a valuable guide.

Willis W. Harman
President, Institute of Noetic Sciences
Sausalito, California
August, 1994

Table of Contents

The allegorical nature of the book is described, and the two main characters introduced (Explorer and Space-Holder). Two caveats are presented: one about the universal masculine pronouns used throughout; the other about the answers eventually found by Explorer not being ultimate answers for everyone.

Explorer encounters a dangerous situation which demands that he quit drifting and take a spiritual stand that will enable him to move forward and have authority in his life. He learns that an assumption is a structured concept which he can use as a "paddle" to propel him on his journey. He asks his friend and coach, Space-Holder, for guidance in selecting such an assumption. Space-Holder describes the possibility of using "self-as-source" as the initial assumption. Explorer examines his considerations about assuming self-as-source, and finally elects to do so.

Explorer wonders what assumptions should follow self-as-source. Space-Holder describes the Question-Answer Process through which potential new assumptions are found. He also explains the key operating principle that truth is defined as the assumption that works best in the situation at hand. He coaches Explorer in doing the Question-Answer Process. Two Tables are presented:

Explorer finds himself paralyzed by fear. Space-Holder explains about two kinds of energy: bad, agitated energy and good, calming energy. The agitated energy must be cleared before the calming energy can be invoked. Agitated energy is cleared by asking oneself for the inaccurate assumption generating it, then finding and substituting the calming assumption. Explorer voices his resistance, but eventually calms himself with a true assumption.

Chapter 4 Doldrums: No Energy for Paddling

Although now calm, Explorer finds himself without any energy to move forward in life. Space-Holder presents the principles about how to bring nurturing energy into the calm space. He defines "transilient" and "transfixing" assumptions and gives examples in Table III. The transilient assumptions are the ones which generate this "good" energy. The problem of Self-as-source versus God-as-source arises, and Space-Holder declares the resolving principle: "Self is the source of all assumptions, including the transilient ones that enable a person to experience the universe's energy whose source is God." He further expounds the principle that present transilient good in the moment is senior to transfixed (good) goals in the future, and that transilient good is the source for healing when transfixed goals do not work.

Chapter 5 Burnout from Over-Running One's Desire for the Goal

Explorer exhausts himself by inappropriately using energy, derived from desire for his goal, to work toward it. This creates addictions and burnout. Space-Holder explains the problem as one using too many transfixed assumptions at one time. He expounds on how this use of desire-energy is just as dysfunctional as using fearful, agitated energy. He supports his view with a quote from Mother Teresa. Explorer works through his dilemma with the Question-Answer Process.

Chapter 6 Emotional Storms Arise en Route, Raining Agitation

Even in normal life, emotional storms of agitated energy arise many times a day. Explorer finds that a responsible way of coping is to use the Question-Answer Process to find and use calming assumptions. Space-Holder points out that this may involve reliving past trauma and renegotiating past decisions.

Chapter 7 Evil Pirates Attack the Boat

Outside human forces intrude destructively in Explorer's life. Space-Holder coaches his friend in defending and distancing himself from such forces. Space-Holder also presents a definition of evil which helps Explorer learn to differentiate evil pirates from drowning victims deserving of help. He also learns to set boundaries, and to be willing to label as evil the perpetrators who are sourced in inaccurate assumptions about their own lack of goodness.

Chapter 8   Excessive Zeal Turns Away Listeners   57

Explorer repels his listeners by his over-zealous attitude when he tries to enroll them in his new philosophy. Space-Holder teaches Explorer about the six roles in life in which transfixing and transilient assumptions are balanced, using Table V. Explorer has been using too many transfixed assumptions during his communications with people. Space-Holder also points out the adverse effects from holding an excessively transfixed ideal (Western Culture) or an excessively transilient ideal (Eastern Culture). He helps Explorer to seek and identify which assumptions are necessary for a particular task at hand.

Chapter 9   Futile Attempts to Paddle with the Sail   65

Space-Holder finds Explorer mired down in heavy marsh grass, and futilely attempting to paddle with the sail. Space-Holder brings out the six balanced roles again, to teach how to select the appropriate role for the task at hand. Explorer discovers how to ascertain which are the essential, transfixed assumptions to accomplish a given job. He works through his reluctance to strive, now that it is appropriate, and learns how to do it without burning out.

Chapter 10   Subversive Crewmember Makes Holes
in Hull   73

Explorer and his newly adopted crew are in despair about their boat suddenly developing holes in the hull (breaks in their sense of what is true) which they suspect were made by one of the crew. Space-Holder points out that this is caused by a crew member telling lies to the others, thus fracturing their view of reality (the boat). Explorer uses the Question-Answer Process to work through the agony and confusion of his resulting "battered reality", and his reluctance to label one of the crew as a "lying perpetrator". The process is completed by reestablishing intact his personal view of truth and handling his fear of this happening again.

Chapter 11   Boat in Storm Shattered on Rocks
of Traumatic Events   85

Explorer's loved one is killed in a storm, shattering him emotionally. Space-Holder coaches Explorer in the two-step process, first handling the battered reality, and then healing the "shattered good story". First, factual truth is reestablished in those areas in which Explorer could not believe the traumatic events had happened. Secondly, he works to restore a sense of meaning in his life by resting in the "dry dock" of transilient good.

his own attempt at creating a spiritual support group, and coaches Explorer in doing the Question-Answer Process as he works through this trauma. Explorer concludes that while such groups are difficult to maintain, they are of great value and worth the risk of future disappointments.

Introduction

This is a story of an inner journey—a prototype of a journey which awaits us all. During my twenty-five years as a practicing psychiatrist I came to have profound respect for the untapped inner knowing available to my patients—and to myself. Very early, I sought and found a way for an individual to develop this inner knowing as his or her own true guide to a productive life and spiritual fulfillment. I applied it as the pivotal principle for seeking and refining my own understanding of the psyche and how we function. This book is the result of that search.

This allegorical tale takes place on the creek of life. The story unfolds as a dialogue between two characters, a spiritual adventurer named "Explorer," and his coach, named "Space-Holder." Explorer represents all of us, the Everyman, one who is "in for the whole catastrophe" of life, as Zorba the Greek philosophized. Space-Holder represents wisdom and experience, and in truth, each of us functions from time-to-time as either Explorer or Space-Holder.

I've written the book in easy-to-read narrative form, so it can be appreciated by seekers of deeper understanding without being too simplistic for professionals. For people in crisis, the friendly camaraderie found in the narrative should engage their attention, and the story line lead them into the principles and concepts in a smoothly readable way. Such readers will be able to readily identify with the difficulties encountered by the main character, Explorer. The processes which he goes through will inspire some to begin carrying out and recording their own processes. It will also give them permission to expand their repertoire of possible assumptions about life issues, which is a prerequisite to their healing. Already, several people who were experiencing personal crises, and who have read the draft manuscript, have made statements ranging from "it was incredibly valuable to me," to "it saved my life." The book is not meant to replace appropriate psychotherapy, but to augment it.

For readers who are spiritual seekers, and are lost in a muddle of conflicting paradoxical viewpoints, the book's step-by-step analysis of how a person creates the structure and quality of inner reality can offer functional clarity about their spiritual journey.

The book is based on actual personal case histories that I have encountered in my practice. The legal and ethical problems, which might arise from the use of clinical case material and the need for confidentiality, are circumvented by employing fictional characters encountering generic problems.

For simplicity, references in the text to Explorer and the other characters, including God, use masculine pronouns throughout. This universal masculine is, however, intended to refer to all of us, regardless of gender. An additional caveat: the inner processes done by Explorer, his particular answers to his questions, are meant to exemplify the principles of the process and show a range of possibilities; they are not meant to be the ultimate answers for everyone.

The seven tables presented in the text are reprinted at the beginning of the Appendix, for ready reference. The Appendix also includes a glossary of terms and a brief history of the development of the principles presented in the text.

Bon voyage!

Mary Hughes Allen, M.D.
Menlo Park, California
December, 1994

Chapter 1

Up a Spiritual Creek Without a Paddle

The sudden roar of upcoming rapids causes Explorer to sit bolt upright. He has been floating along in a little boat on his spiritual journey wherever the creek's current takes him. Now that he hears rapids ahead, he's confronting the folly of having no paddle with which to steer or propel it. He can't see around the approaching bend, but the current is noticeably increasing in speed. Explorer feels a clutch of panic as he hears shouts from other boaters who have oars and who have just paddled upstream from the rapids ahead. They call out to warn him of the impending danger.

The speed of the stream increases even more and Explorer looks around frantically for assistance. With a great surge of relief, he spots his old friend and spiritual coach, Space-Holder, who is just tying his boat to a pier some distance away. Explorer whistles and yells to get Space-Holder's attention.

Space-Holder lifts his head and scans the stream. He waves back as he recognizes Explorer. Explorer yells and desperately motions that he needs to be rescued and towed to shore. Space-Holder quickly jumps back into his boat, unties the line and skillfully paddles on a track that will meet the drifting Explorer. As their boats approach, Space-Holder deftly throws his line to Explorer and with strong strokes, begins to overcome the current and pull him toward the bank. A wave of relief comes over Explorer, and he sighs in amazement at his luck.

As the boats reach shallow water, the current lessens to the point where both men can jump out and tether their boats to convenient rocks. Explorer looks embarrassed, but Space-Holder gives him a hug in greeting and suggests they sit down on a nearby grassy slope to talk.

Explorer thanks his old friend for the timely rescue and admits that he is now in urgent need of choosing some kind of "paddle" (structured belief) to give him direction in his life. In the past, Explorer followed a policy of listening and collecting data from various spiritual teachers, while remaining aloof and uncommitted to any particular paddle in his spiritual quest. To him, this had the advantage of leaving him open to hear all kinds of different ideas. "I felt I wouldn't miss anything important that way," he explains, "yet approaching those rapids with no paddle convinces me I have to make a major choice. Meeting you at this point is really fortuitous."

Explorer sees clearly that his present situation demonstrates his lack of personal power and authority to move himself in a chosen direction. He knows from past discussions that Space-Holder guides his own life in a way that reflects strong principles. He needs to hear about those principles again, so he can decide whether to commit himself to Space-Holder's type of paddle.

"Tell me about your paddle," says Explorer, "and how can I best decide which type to choose?"

Space-Holder muses over the question, then turns to face his friend. "Many people," he says, "choose for themselves the beliefs in whose atmosphere they grew up; or rebelling against those, adopt the beliefs held by their friends or role models whose lives they admire. You have passed beyond those stages—there are many people you admire all of whom have different beliefs. I can see you're looking for a more specific basis for your choice. All I can offer you is my own experience in the matter. Perhaps that will give you enough insight to enable you to make a decision."

"How did you make your choice?" asks Explorer.

Space-Holder gazes off over the creek and waves away a pesky insect. He turns back and says, "I was in a situation similar to your own. I discovered that my personal well-being depended on committing myself to some particular belief in order to be able to act with power and authority in my life. There were lots of popular ones being tried by many people but in my observation none seemed to be working very well. I put a lot of thought into it over the months and came up with a new way that I hoped would be more effective. If it didn't work so well, I knew that reporting it as a failure would be valuable to others so they wouldn't bother to try that way in the future. If it succeeded, I knew it would be useful to a lot of other travelers and therefore worth the risk that always comes from trying something new. Since you, also, haven't taken up any of the old popular ways, perhaps joining me in experimenting with this new approach might be worthwhile."

Trying something new appeals to Explorer's sense of adventure. He feels a renewed enthusiasm welling up and encourages Space-Holder to describe how he launched his new system.

"Any religion, philosophy, or even psychological belief system," declares Space-Holder, "has a beginning point from which everything else is viewed. It has one particular belief or assumption as its keystone—a fundamental element as the source out of which flows everything else in the philosophy. It's interesting that all the rest of the beliefs in the system are limited by the choice of a particular source. Why? Because questions about anything more fundamental than the source are forbidden as being outside the frame of reference. Of course, the derivation of every other aspect of the system may be questioned. And certain of the derivatives may be only provisionally true in a given situation, but within the confines of that philosophical or psychological system, the designated source is always true and taken for granted."

Explorer nods with enthusiasm, but realizes he has only a tenuous understanding of what Space-Holder has just described. Space-Holder pauses, giving the words a chance to sink in. Then he continues.

"In choosing a belief system, it is very important to be aware of its designated source. We want it to cast the smallest possible shadow of forbidden questions, and to have the shadow not obscure any of the vital areas in which we wish to work. For instance, if we want to know what generates something, such as feelings, we cannot use feelings as the source, because questions about what generates the source are forbidden and unanswerable in the system.

"I think it would be useful here," continues Space-Holder, "to look at some examples of existing systems and notice what element is in the role of source in each. Later, I'll explain my new system and its source. But first, let's use some well known psychological systems and a religious one for examples: Cognitive Therapy, Behavioral Therapy, Patient-Centered (Supportive) Therapy, Transpersonal Therapy, 'Experiential' Therapy and Religious Healing. Let's examine each in turn."

"**Cognitive Therapy**—The practitioners of this approach view people's troubles and symptoms as caused by certain of their irrational or dysfunctional beliefs. In this view the source of the power of healing is the modification of the beliefs to more functional substitutes. The therapy involves the laborious ferreting out of unconsciously-held beliefs and the exploration of replacements. So here, a person's *assumptions* are source or starting point.

"**Behavioral Therapy**—Here, practitioners hold the view that if a person behaves correctly, they will be healed. Correct action in the world, including proper behavior or taking appropriate medication, will result in a primary shift toward health. Thus, a person's *behavior and actions* are viewed as source.

"Patient-Centered (Supportive) Therapy—Practitioners of this therapy believe that if they create a loving enough atmosphere, with caring and empathy, their clients will be cured through this corrective, emotional experience. Here, the person's *sense of being loved* is viewed as source.

"Transpersonal Therapy—Along with more conventional approaches, these practitioners bring in the spiritual dimension as a reality and as a primary source of healing. In their effort to include all spiritual traditions, transpersonal therapists tend to the view that none of the traditions have the absolute answer. In their frame of reference, the source might be called *unitary consciousness.*

"'Experiential' Therapy—The various approaches included in this category have in common the use of the person's inner experience as the primary focus. Examples include the use of imagery, archetypes, dreams, art, music, psychedelics, mystical experience, guided imagery, etc. The source of healing is assumed to come from spontaneous, *inner experiences.*

"Religious Healers—In religious traditions, stories about reality, truth and goodness, or the statements of great religious figures, are shared in a community with a collective spiritual viewpoint, handed down from generation to generation. The person's shared *myths, stories and principles* are viewed as the source or starting point of healing.

"All of the above approaches to healing have their place," states Space-Holder, "but each has limitations. I was looking for a source or starting point from which a philosophy could be generated that would both encompass and go beyond them all."

Explorer is all ears, listening intently to discover what particular source Space-Holder had selected for his experiment. "If it is everything you are saying it is," Explorer declares, "it sounds like something worth trying."

Space-Holder proceeds with his exposition: "After long periods of questioning and wrestling with the possibilities,

I settled on the following premise to be the beginning point of my new philosophy:

"The nearest experience a person can have of source in that person's life, is that person's own experience of *self*.

"I named this premise 'self-as-source'. The self that I am talking about is not some remote concept such as 'ego', nor any higher order Self with a capital S that we spend our lives trying to be without ever really reaching. What I am speaking of is any person's ordinary experience of being 'me' when the person is relaxed and not being anything in particular.

"It is a fairly audacious idea that this ordinary, every-day experience—available to each of us—could be so important and brimming with potential as to be the source and starting point of a whole philosophy. Historically, it has been hinted at, in such stories as God's telling Moses that God's name is 'I am that I am', or Bible teachings about man being made in the image of God, or the Hindu saying about Atman being Brahman, or the Buddha-nature being present in us all. But in no popular philosophy has the little ordinary human 'me' in each of us been assumed to be the highest and most powerful source in the universe. Such an outrageous idea! Yet I felt compelled to experiment with it and see where it would lead.

"In the years since beginning this experiment, I have asked and found answers for such questions as 'What are the abilities of this self that I am?' 'How does it function in the universe?' 'What is it responsible for?' 'How does it interact with other such selves?' 'Where does God fit into this philosophy?' But my answers to most of those questions can wait for another day.

"The point for today is that there are two main attributes of this self, one active and one passive. The active one is that the self makes assumptions about what is true. The passive one is that the self is aware of experience as it arises. The self is in charge of choosing which assumptions to make and can make them and unmake them at will just by saying, 'If I assume for a while that this idea is true, what happens?' In other words, just by trying it on for size.

"On the other hand in the passive function, experiences spontaneously arise. The self is in charge of paying attention and being aware of them but is not conscious of being in charge of making or generating them.

"To give you an example of how this works, let's look at the assumptions that spontaneously arise in your experience when you consider adopting the self-as-source premise. Then notice how you can change the old assumptions that arise into new ones that might be more compatible with the new starting point. Just notice what words come into your mind when you try to assume self-as-source." Space-Holder pauses to give Explorer time to think.

Explorer closes his eyes, and says to himself softly, "If I assume for the moment, that the closest experience I can have of source in my life is my own experience of myself what ideas arise in my inner experience?" He waits for a few seconds, and then reports to Space-Holder: "It's just too arbitrary to assume that I, myself, am the closest I can come to the divine source of all things!"

Space-Holder grins his approval. "That's a good answer. It is good in the sense that any clear experience that could be put into words would be good. Now decide what else you might assume to be true, which would enable you to feel more comfortable with the self-as-source assumption."

Explorer thinks hard, and finally says, "If I assumed that it was necessary to make self-as-source my primary assumption it might work. If there were no other way to do it, then my feeling that it's too arbitrary probably wouldn't come up."

Space-Holder smiles and settles back to share an analogy: "When I first began experimenting with self-as-source as the initiating idea, I thought of comparing it to the solution which sailors found to the problem of knowing where they were, East to West, on the wide expanse of the ocean. In contrast to their East-West problem, they had, for hundreds of years, known how to tell where they were with respect to North-South latitudes: they could look at the fixed stars, such as the North Star, and determine how far it was above the horizon at night. The higher it was in the sky, the farther north they knew they were. But they would sail for months across the Pacific Ocean without knowing where they were, East-to-West, until they finally landed in Japan.

"Eventually in the 1700's, the chronometer was invented. It was a very accurate clock which they would set and keep running so that they always knew what time it was at one particular place on Earth. Since England was the dominant sea power at the time, the sailors chose Greenwich to be that particular place. As their next step, they laboriously wrote a reference book which listed the position of the sun in the sky over Greenwich at each hour of the day for the whole year. As long as they had their chronometer and the reference book, they could be in the middle of the Pacific Ocean and determine exactly where they were. They'd calculate how far around the Earth they were by how much their view of the sun's position differed from what they knew it was in Greenwich.

"You can see that they would have obtained totally wrong answers to their calculations," Space-Holder chuckles, "if some sailor had decided to set the chronometer to Tokyo time as a 'source' instead of Greenwich time since their reference book was for Greenwich. It is true that they could have originally chosen Tokyo instead of Greenwich, if they had made their reference book for Tokyo. The important thing was to set their chronometer to the local time in the reference book's location.

"In the case of a person who is trying to navigate through life, the most accurate 'reference book' available to him is his own inner experience. If we view each person's inner experience as a personal psychic computer, you can see that one's own computer will have much more appropriate data for yielding accurate answers for that person than anyone else's inner computer. All other reference books, such as holy books or guides to living, are written in contradictions and paradoxes in order to cover all possible contingencies, since they are unable to refer to the particular circumstance the person is in at the moment.

"Thus, it's important and yes—necessary," concludes Space-Holder, "to choose one's self as the absolute starting point—analogous to setting the chronometer to Greenwich time—because each of us has our own inner reference book geared to ourselves."

Though Explorer immediately grasps the relevance of this cogent reason, he has reservations. Closing his eyes and focusing for a minute, he then says, "It seems too arrogant to assume that I myself am the closest I can come to the divine source of all things."

Space-Holder looks down, smiles, scratches his chin and shuffles his feet. "When I first wondered about that, I realized that if I didn't start with the self-as-source principle, there was no way that I would ever arrive at the peak mystical experience I aspired to. It is called the 'I am' experience. In that moment, nobody else exists. I am, and I am everything and everyone. There is no one else to anoint me or elect me or promote me into that experience. If I don't start by assuming it to be true, by making the self-as-source principle my starting point, I cannot ever get there. I don't see it as arrogant to assume this; I see it as absolutely necessary to make that experience available to me."

Explorer nods slowly, the pertinence of this point seeping in. Another consideration then occurs to him: "Will I be too dictatorial and autocratic in my interactions with others if I start with this self-as-source idea as the primary assumption?"

Space-Holder replies, "Not if you trust yourself to be appropriately open and provide for the autonomy of others, just as you wish them to do for you. If there are flaws in how you do this then the flaws will show that you're operating out of some previously-made inaccurate assumptions. These can be experimentally corrected as you learn to do the process better."

The next reluctance that Explorer encounters comes from his humble nature: "My own self is too ordinary, and does not have the fire and glory which I associate with the divine."

Space-Holder looks him straight in the eye and replies, "It is true that your ordinary self is not much of anything in particular, but that's the beauty of sources: They seem like nothing much, and then everything springs forth from them. The appearance of a source is not the criterion for its validity. Experiment with it, and discover whether it works best to assume it as source—that is the criterion for truth here."

Explorer is surprised by his growing understanding. Nonetheless he raises another objection: "My own self is too flawed, has too many old inaccurate assumptions, doesn't work very well in the world so it's obviously not perfect. As the closest I can get to the divine source, it ought to be more perfect than this."

Space-Holder chuckles, "When I had that thought, it occurred to me that I may not be all that great but that I'm all I've got! It was better to start with my ordinary flawed self than to try to start over with a whole new being. I knew that I could tidy myself up as I went and I could still affirm for myself that I was the most powerful point in the universe that I could play from."

Explorer laughs and decides he isn't too flawed after all. Finally, he comes up with one last objection: "The self-as-source principle seems too simplistic as a starting point for a whole complicated philosophy that will cover everything in the world."

Space-Holder refers to the point he made earlier. "Every philosophy starts somewhere," he begins, "with one primary assumption and builds from there. Every starting point is simple. If one peels back through a philosophy's presuppositions, he arrives at its beginning point which is taken for granted in the philosophy. And every beginning point creates a shadow behind it, a shadow of questions that are taboo and beyond the frame of reference with which that particular philosophy can deal. In the case of the self-as-source starting principle an example of such a taboo question would be: 'Why was self-as-source made the best primary assumption?' The answer to that, from within the system, is either, 'It just is!' or 'That's part of the mystery.'"

Space-Holder continues: "Each spiritual adventurer must find his own unique answers for himself. What I've described are just suggestions from my personal experience. You will gradually find your own answers, and they will constitute your personal mythology. Yours will differ in some ways from every other mythology in the world. The main thing I have learned about personal myths is that there is a multiplicity of them, just as all fruit trees are not created to grow apples. We are not supposed to seek and find the 'one true mythology' in contrast to physicists who are supposed to seek and find the one true law relating a set of physical facts which they can all then agree upon. We are supposed to follow the trail of meaningfulness as it comes up in our experience, and each one of us is to build a unique world view.

"Another thing which I have learned about personal myths," concludes Space-Holder, "is that they flourish best in an experience of communion with other souls, each honoring the other's views. That communion exists in the state of mystery where none of us knows all the answers and where we work to be supportive and loving to each other along the way to discovery."

Explorer stands up in a quiet yet excited mood. He has decided to try self-as-source as his stable paddle in life, and he is eagerly looking forward to his coming adventures. He thanks Space-Holder, and promises to return the next day for another lesson, after he has exercised this one by paddling on the creek for awhile. Space-Holder smiles and wishes him well as they saunter back toward the boats.

Chapter 2

In Mystery about
Where to Go from Here

I don't want to admit it but I'm at a loss," sighs Explorer. During his journey, he has been studying, listening, and experiencing much in the spiritual realm. He has spent hours swimming in beautiful soul-stirring truths in his "creek of life." Many of these truths seem to contradict each other, which puzzles him at times. His recent decision to assume self-as-source to be true and to be his starting point, creates enough structure for him to be able to paddle his little boat where he wishes. Now he is at a loss for what to do next.

There are so many possible ideas to assume to be true as a next step, that his mind boggles at the choices. They all seem potentially wonderful, but if he chooses to assume one to be true, he feels that he is giving up his chance to assume its opposite as true. For example, if he assumes he should be striving, he gives up the possibility of flowing with life. If he assumes first one and then the other and back again, it feels as if he would be going in circles and getting nowhere. To Explorer, it seems he is in a soft fog with no way to decide in which direction to go.

He returns to the shore where his spiritual coach, Space-Holder, has already set up charts and a blackboard, preparing to tutor Explorer in a next-step maneuver. Space-Holder begins by reminding Explorer of the way the physicists handled it when they came up with two theories about the nature of light, each of which contradicted the other. Each theory could be proved true and useful in different experiments. The physicists did not let it boggle their minds. They just admitted to themselves that the human mind was limited and did not know the absolute truth about the nature of light. They decided to keep both theories in their toolbox and to use the one that worked best in whatever experiment they were doing at the time.

The physicists use the particle theory of light in photoelectric experiments and the wave theory of light in diffraction experiments. Their criterion of what to assume to be true at the moment is based on whichever theory works best in the given situation.

Explorer remembers his physics class and how the physicists had not been stymied by having two contradictory truths to use. The physicists knew that who they were was "bigger" (more primary) than their toolbox. They knew that they were in command of which theory to use. But notwithstanding that, Explorer was still at a loss to know which spiritual assumption to make at any given time. The physicists had already done all these experiments and they knew which theory was likely to work in which experiment. How could Explorer know which one to use?

With a flourish, Space-Holder reaches into his toolbox and pulls out his most prized and useful technique, the Question-Answer Process. He instructs Explorer in its use, saying that this is a tool through which any human can gain access to his own "personal spiritual computer." Space-Holder explains that the computer has been programmed in the past, whenever the person has experienced something and drawn a conclusion about how the world works. It can be re-programmed by the person's deciding to draw a different conclusion (a new assumption) and then trying it in daily life to gain new data. The personal inner computer also has a tie into the main cosmic computer network, (that the Hindus named the "Akashic Record") plus cross ties to other beings' personal inner computers. All

Explorer has to do is direct a question to the computer network.

Space-Holder shows Explorer a chart (see Table I) listing the steps of the Question-Answer Process. He proceeds to coach Explorer in doing the process.

TABLE I:

Steps of the Question-Answer Process

Step One: Get a Question

Notice something you are curious about and form a specific question about it.

Step Two: I Don't Know

Let go into an experience of "I don't know." Don't try to figure it out logically.

Step Three: An Answer

Notice the next experience that comes up. It may be words in your mind's ear, or pictures in your mind's eye, or an emotion, or a sensation in your body. If "I don't know" is what comes up, look at the next thing which comes up after that in your experience.

Step Four: Assume the Answer to be True

Put whatever came up in Step 3 into words, and for the moment, assume it to be the true answer to the question. If the answer in Step 3 were true, what would be your next question? Go on repeating the four steps until there is some clarity about the area of the questions. Then step back and decide what assumption to experimentally assume to be true for the next few days.

Space-Holder explains that his function would be to write down the questions and answers as they came up for Explorer. "If the person is doing the process alone," he remarks, "the person himself takes the time to write them down. The reason for writing them is that it is often hard to recall the train of thought of the questions after the first few have been answered. What is your first question, Explorer? What are you curious about? If you had a book of questions and answers from the oracles, what would you look up?" He explains that if no question immediately comes to mind, that Explorer should be like a surfer on a surf board, waiting for the next wave. "Wait for your next wondering, and then notice what you are wondering about."

Explorer frowns a little, closes his eyes, and asks himself what he is curious about. The first question that comes to mind is, "Is this process going to work?"

Space-Holder requests that Explorer describe his next inner experience. Explorer says that the words come up "I don't know." Space-Holder asks Explorer to notice the next experience after the "I don't know"—just whatever his gut-feel is. Explorer says that he has a hopeful feeling of "Yes." Space-Holder beams, "Good; that is a clear answer; any clear answer would be correct in the sense of being useful. For the moment, assume that this is the true answer to your question. Ask yourself: 'If that is true, what is my next question?'"

Explorer wonders, "Where do these answers come from?" Space-Holder suggests that Explorer look at his own answer to that question first. Explorer declares, "The answers come from within me; where they come from before that, I'm not sure. Perhaps I'm in touch by extrasensory perception to the cosmic computer or some wise spirit who knows."

Space-Holder then produces Table II, a list of some examples of the possible sources of the answers. He directs Explorer to see if he can think of any additional sources that might be possible.

TABLE II

Possible Source of Answers

1 . One's own personal mental computer, including memories of experiences and a stack of operating assumptions.

2 . Universal mental computer, also called by some the Akashic Record or "Mind", having been defined as the "multi-sensory, linear, recorded instants of now."[1]

3 . Extrasensory perception (e.s.p.) of another incarnate person's personal mental computer.

4 . Extrasensory perception of a discarnate person's mental computer.

5 . One's Higher Self, or Soul, or God, or All-knowing Wisdom.

6 . Higher beings who are fellow travelers on our path. Examples include: Angels, Moses, Jesus, Buddha, Mary, Gabriel, guides.

Explorer does not have any additional examples of sources to add to the list, but he has a new question: "How can I trust these answers to be true?"

Space-Holder instructs Explorer to look for his next experience as an answer, following the steps of the Question-Answer Process. Explorer recounts, "I can trust that the answer is what my computer, or someone else's computer has as true in its program. I realize that I have to test it in my life situation to see if it is the one that works best for me and is therefore true for me now."

Space-Holder smiles approvingly at his charge and indicates he should look for his next question. Explorer continues, giving both questions and answers:

Why am I at a loss—up this spiritual creek without a paddle?

Too many confusing and contradicting ideas in my mind. I need to center in and focus on one question and one answer at a time.

What is my next question?

Where do I want to go?

My final destination is to go home—back to source.

What is my interim destination that I want to go to now?

I want to go to the town of Comfort Corners where I can get some spiritual nurturing for myself.

What do I need in order to select that destination?

I need to assume that it exists—that I have the power to paddle myself there and that this is where I should go. I notice that I am afraid it might be too self-indulgent and lazy to go somewhere just because it feels good.

Space-Holder interjects: "You are doing fine. Do you have a question about your last observation? Just continue to do the Question-Answer Process whenever you have a question or are feeling confused."

Explorer continues:

Would it be too self-indulgent to go to Comfort Corners?

Not at this time when I am feeling in great need of spiritual nurturing.

Can I trust myself to judge this correctly?

If not, I will find out by trying it. If I find that I'm being too self-indulgent in the future I can explore the problem then, changing some assumptions, and experimenting with the new ones. As I gain more experience, I add to my personal mental computer's data base. New experiences may lead to new answers coming up for me next time. This is all part of my journey—I only have to make one decision at a time.

What is the spiritual lesson that I am trying to learn here?

To learn that I myself am the source of my assumptions about reality and that assumptions are useful structuring things to use as paddles. I can use them to propel and steer me toward my goal. If my current assumptions don't work I can correct them and try new ones. Being the source of my assumptions puts me in charge of my game plan.

Is there anything I am not the source of?

I don't know. (Pauses to let the next experience arise.) Next I feel a huge empty space with energy flowing through it.

Who or what is the source of this space and energy?

God is the source of the energy but I have to open myself to it by making some assumptions that make the connection possible. Therefore I am the source of my connection to the energetic force for good. God is the source of the energy.

Explorer opens his eyes and says, "Hey I can do this!" "Of course," replies Space-Holder, "it's an innate ability in all of us—actually it's the natural way we think. These more formal steps just help us move through it if we're hesitant or bogged down."

Explorer stands and stretches. "I think I'm ready to go off and try this for awhile."

Space-Holder waves as Explorer leaves, cheerfully paddling off for Comfort Corners, playing with his new assumption paddles.

Chapter 3

Paralyzed by Fearful Agitated Energy

Explorer is having fun with his new assumptions—creating them, trying them and discarding those that didn't work. He is feeling renewed authority in directing his movement from place to place on the stream until some nightmarish ideas occur to him: What if he is supposed to be more diligent and not so playful? Will he be labeled a failure if he just putters around and doesn't pursue any more significant spiritual goal? Will his old neurotic habit patterns rear their heads and drag him down into a whirlpool he could never get out of? Are there alligators or water vipers lurking and ready to attack him?

Explorer becomes so agitated by these frightening thoughts that he frantically tries to paddle in many directions at once, and then gives up. He begins drifting in a hopeless and immobilized state, paralyzed by fear.

Again, Space-Holder comes to the rescue with his charts and blackboard. He waves his arms and hollers to get Explorer's attention. Explorer turns his wide frightened eyes toward Space-Holder who is watching from the bank, though he feels hopeless that anyone could have an answer for this problem.

Space-Holder props up a chart with big words on it: "There are two kinds of energy: One agitated and bad and the other calm and good."

Explorer wonders at this idea. He has never thought much about the nature of the life force's energy flowing through him. He has been like a fish who had never thought much about the water he was in. Explorer has just taken it for granted that different qualities of energies and emotions came up in him, seemingly out of his control. It excites him to think that there might be two kinds of energy, and that he might have some choice about which kind he experiences. He wants to talk about this further, so he paddles over to the shore, beaches the boat and climbs up the bank to where Space-Holder has set up a canvas covering for shade.

Space-Holder continues his lesson by describing a possible way the universe might work. He says, "Suppose there was a way for a human being to sense what was true. For instance, what if you could sense the truth of whether or not there really were dangerous alligators poised to strike you. What if the universe was so constructed that a human being could sense truth in the same way he could sense warmth or cold, light or dark. And further, what if the way that this truth-sensing worked was: first, to imagine what might be true; second, to try it on for size by, for the moment, assuming it to be true; and third, to notice what experience came up at that point. Was it a calm open feeling, or was it a jolt resulting from the 'universe' kicking that assumption out of the person's computer? The calm experience would indicate that the idea the person was assuming was true for now. The 'jolting out' of the assumption would indicate the idea was false.

"In this system a person still has the choice about whether to assume the false idea to be true. A person can insist, 'I am sure there are alligators here' when there are none. And the more the universe tries to jolt it out of the person's computer, the more the person insists and pushes the assumption back in place. This alternate jolting out and insisting back in will result in a back and forth shaking which might be called 'the fearful agitated energy of an inaccurate assumption'. If a person insists strongly enough, he can drive himself right up the wall with frantic agitation. He can do it so hard that he would have to be practically anesthetized before he will let go, relax, and start over with some truer, and therefore calmer, assumption."

Explorer follows this conjecture but finds himself arguing with Space-Holder by saying, "How do you know? Can you prove there are no alligators in this creek?"

Space-Holder patiently points out that he can prove nothing, but neither can Explorer. All either of them has is a sense of calm when they assume no danger from alligators, and a sense of agitation when they assume imminent danger from alligators.

Explorer argues, "Assuming the calming idea to be true might just be wishful thinking. I think I should assume the agitating frightening idea to be true just to be on the safe side."

Space-Holder points out that it is not very safe to immobilize oneself with fear. In fact, it is very debilitating. He reminds Explorer of times in his student years when he would scare himself into studying for a test with visions of the awful things that would surely happen if he failed. Space-Holder quotes the general principle that the only useful function of agitated energy is as a warning signal that there is an inaccurate assumption that needs tidying and correcting. Using agitated energy as a motive for paddling in the creek is more debilitating than it is worth in almost all circumstances.

Explorer takes the idea one step further. "What if a person really was being attacked by alligators? Then should he be afraid?"

Space-Holder reminds Explorer of that time when Explorer's life was in imminent danger from an on-coming car driven by a drunk driver going the wrong way on the freeway. Explorer recalls that he had been amazed at how calm he was in the moment; how time had passed so slowly as he took evasive action. It was afterward that he had felt fear. Space-Holder points out that the fear was an agitated energy generated by his thinking inaccurately of the frightening things that might have happened but didn't.

Explorer shifts the focus to people who have an incurable life-threatening disease, such as cancer. "Should not the person be afraid of dying?" he asks.

Space-Holder reminds Explorer of the work of death and dying counselors such as Elizabeth Kübler-Ross. They describe a process that includes working through agitated stages and finally reaching acceptance and peace with the truth as the last stage in facing dying.

Explorer can't argue with that. He begins experimenting with this new view. The fact is that he might actually be receiving a sensation which could indicate whether what he was assuming was actually true. He easily sees that assuming "no alligators" is more calming and good for his general well being if there really is no danger. But the minute he starts to think that there really might be alligators, he is all agitated again.

Space-Holder tells him that this type of "catastrophizing" was common. Some people misinterpreted the "jolting of the universe"—really indicating "this is not true"—to be a sign that the catastrophe will happen. They misused the warning indicator. In fact, many times they actually thought they could feel the catastrophe happening and up the wall they went.

Explorer acknowledges that he is probably guilty of doing that. The agitation did feel a little like an alligator tearing at his body. And he can see the error in becoming so riled up that he is immobilized with terror and can do nothing constructive about his situation. Explorer is still concerned that if he only assumes things that makes him calm, he will have no energy to do the things he needs to do in life.

Space-Holder says this is enough of a lesson for today. Tomorrow they can explore the principles that will enable Explorer to increase the amount of good energy in the calm experience. In the meantime, Space-Holder recommends that Explorer make only calming assumptions that will nurture him. In time, it will restore his well-being which has been so damaged by the agitated energy.

Chapter 4

Doldrums: No Energy for Paddling

The next day, Explorer has recuperated from his experience with agitated energy, and is feeling better. However, though he feels calm, he has little energy with which to do anything. He eagerly awaits Space-Holder's next lesson on how to create good energy in his calm state.

Space-Holder shows up in an outlandishly comical outfit carrying a big leather bag that holds more charts. "Just to lighten up the mood with a little humor," he chuckles. As Explorer laughs, he notices that his energy picks up somewhat and he is encouraged that this lesson might really work for him. He settles down to listen as Space-Holder extracts two charts and chalkboard from the bag.

"Let's go back," Space-Holder begins, "to those confusingly contradictory assumptions that we spoke of in the first lesson. The physicists have names for their two contradictory theories: The wave theory and the particle theory. And they call these paradoxes 'complementary contraries.' Why, you ask? Both are needed to complement and complete each other in order to express the whole truth as best they can understand it.

"Try postulating that there would be at least two contradictory, complementary assumptions a person could make about himself, when thinking about any of the four holistic aspects—mind, body, emotions, and spirit. Among the infinite number of possible assumptions, Table III

TABLE III

Pairs of Transilient and Transfixing
Assumptions about Myself

("I am . . .)

ASPECTS OF ME	TRANSFIXING ASSUMPTIONS	TRANSILIENT ASSUMPTIONS
MIND	*. . . Knowing"*	*. . . In Mystery"*
	I live in a knowable world where it's possible to figure out anything.	I live in a mysterious, wondrous universe, unknowable in its entirety.
SPIRIT	*. . . Uniquely Individual"*	*. . . In Empathy & Kinship"*
	I am a unique, separate, individual, viable being.	I am one with all, in empathy and kinship with all creation.
BODY	*. . . Striving"*	*. . . Relaxing in Safety"*
	I need to strive hard to survive and succeed in this physical world.	I am relaxed and trust that my existence is supported by the eternal universe.
EMOTIONS	*. . . In a Good Story"*	*. . . Just Being Now"*
	I focus on my vision of the future good which is better than what is now.	All the good that exists is present in this moment and available if I open to it.

NOTE: At the end of the chapter, Table IV is presented with "over-run" conditions which result when an assumption is used beyond the time when it is effective.

presents a basic pair that would most powerfully show the scope of each holistic aspect."

"Each complementary pair of assumptions," Space-Holder continues, "are analogous to the wave and particle theories of light. There are two terms used to describe the members of the pair: *The assumption analogous to the wave theory is called "transilient" because it creates an energy field; the assumption corresponding to the particle theory is called "transfixing" because it gives structure to reality.*

"Let's look at these words more closely. 'Transilient' is related to the word 'resilient' which refers to bouncing back to an original shape. Transilient refers to bouncing out of, over, or beyond (trans) the original. It has been used mostly by botanists to describe seed pods which spontaneously burst open and spew forth seeds. As you read through Table III, notice how the transilient assumptions create more energy in your experience. Eventually, when you want more energy, all you have to do is shift more of your assumptions into the transilient mode. As a general principle, it is best to have some of your assumptions be transilient and some be transfixing at any given time. This results in both energy and structure.

"Let me start in the mind aspect, since we are being so mental and theoretical about all this. The transfixing or structuring assumption is that I am a being who lives in a knowable world. Given enough time, energy and money, I could figure out anything that exists. You will recognize here a scientific view of the world.

"The contrary assumption, which is more transilient, opening, and energizing, is that I am a being who lives in a mysterious, wondrous universe that is intrinsically unknowable, and not to know is all right. Keep in mind that a person's job is to assume whichever assumption works best in the situation at hand. Thus, when I'm doing my income taxes, I will do better to assume that the world is knowable, but when I am romantically in love it works better to assume the world is mysterious and wondrous.

"The next pair of complementary contrary assumptions are in the spirit aspect: The transfixing assumption is that I am a unique separate individual being. I am a distinct entity coming from my unique viewpoint into the world.

"In contrast, the transilient assumption in the spirit aspect is that I am a being who is one with all, in empathy and kinship with everyone and everything. When I need to be a strong, solid, assertive individual in the work-a-day world, I naturally would do better to be in the transfixing mode; when I am relating intimately with my significant other, the empathic transilient mode usually works best.

"In the body aspect, the transfixing assumption is that I am a being who needs to strive hard to survive and succeed in this physical world. By contrast, the transilient assumption is that I am a playful immortal spirit with unlimited time in which to accomplish anything, so I can relax in the safety of eternity.

"The fourth holistic aspect, the emotions, refers to our value systems—to what we love and desire—what we're about—and to what we designate as good. My life can be viewed as a myth or a 'story' in which I function. The transfixed assumption is that the story in which I live is about what is good—called for short, a 'good story'— this story extends from the past into the future. Something in the future is designated by each of us as being better than what exists in the present, and is therefore worth working toward.

"In contrast, the transilient assumption in the emotion aspect is that I am a being who only exists in the 'Now.' The past is but a memory, the future but a fantasy. All the good that exists is present in this moment, available to me if I open to it. Being open to it means not judging the experience as good or bad, but just being with it in the moment. This good experience includes, in the outer world—the sun in the morning and the moon at night—the trees and grass and flowers and sky. In the inner world it includes the mystical depths of my being in which I can be in touch with the aliveness of the universe—the life force which permeates everything and everyone, creating the best and highest good for all concerned."

Explorer is following Space-Holder's lecture well, though it is a lot of data to absorb all at once. He is glad that Table III there to scan in order to keep it all in mind.

Space-Holder continues his presentation by describing an odd thing about truth which experimenting with these complementary contrary assumptions has made clear. "It turns out," said Space-Holder, "that the way the truth about goodness works is opposite from the way that the truth about facts works. This 'oppositeness' is as dramatic and real as the opposite way that an airplane's controls work, once the plane is going faster than the speed of sound.

"Many test pilots were killed in breaking the sound barrier; they never pulled out of the dives that they put their planes into to get going that fast. Finally, Chuck Yaeger tried it, and reported later that he found that the usual pulling back on the stick would not bring the nose of the plane up from the dive. He decided to try anything to see what might save him from crashing. He tried the opposite, pushing the stick away from him, which at ordinary speeds would have driven the nose of the plane even further into the dive toward the ground. To his amazement and relief, the nose pulled up, and he became the first test pilot to survive breaking the sound barrier. Thus, he learned that when going faster than the speed of sound, the controls on an airplane reverse function.

"A similar reversal occurs," continued Space-Holder, "when we shift from working with the truth about facts, such as whether there are alligators in the creek, to working with the truth about value systems and goodness. In the last lesson, you learned that you could create a nurturing calmness instead of agitated energy, by assuming the true facts to be true. Amazingly, the opposite is true when dealing with goodness. The calming experience is created by assuming that the desired good goal already exists in spite of facts to the contrary. Otherwise, we leak a lot of good energy longing for that good which is not yet in existence.

"This is not a new discovery. Jesus spoke of it almost two thousand years ago when he said, 'Whatever you ask for in prayer, believe that you have received it, and it will be yours.' [Mark 11:24 (N.I.V.)]

"There is one more very important difference," continued Space-Holder, "between our experience of physical fact and our experience of goodness: With physical fact, the (transfixed) physical world is a given. Molecules exist as the beginning point, and we create in the world by rearranging them. By contrast, in the realm of goodness, the beginning point is transilient rather than transfixed. That which is senior to, exists before, and is the source of goodness, is that which is in the non-physical realm of transilient good.

"The force for good, in consensus with each of us, generates our physical (transfixed) good out of the transilient good in the moment, unfolding it into our future in the physical world."

Explorer interjects a question: "How does this fit with our starting assumption of self-as-source? This sounds like transilient good is source."

Space-Holder suggests to Explorer that he use the Question-Answer Process to take a look at the principles involved.

Explorer closes his eyes and centers himself. He asks, "What am I source of, and what is God or transilient good the source of?" The answer comes: "I, myself, am source of the assumptions that structure my reality. These assumptions include the transilient ones that open me to an experience of transilient good (or God) as the source of my energy".

Space-Holder nods agreement and comments, "You can see why a researcher trained as a physical scientist would find it very difficult to conceive of the way that the transilient assumption in the emotion aspect works. It is as much outside such a researcher's realm of possibilities as was Chuck Yaeger's discovery that the airplane controls reverse function above the speed of sound. The proof of the pudding is in the eating, however. Chuck Yaeger is alive and the earlier test pilots are dead. Try these assumptions, experiment with them and observe whether they work best. Remember, 'what works best' is our criterion for the truth of an assumption.

"So how can you apply this discussion," continues Space-Holder, "to creating more transilient energy with which to paddle your boat? You could jump start some energy by assuming all four transilient assumptions at once. However, it is more functional and practical to have half of your assumptions from Table III be transfixed at any one time. The important thing, as an exercise, is to vividly create the transilient ones as true, and have them readily available in your tool box. The general principle is that if you want more energy in the calm space you created, make the transilient assumptions more real for yourself.

"For instance, if you assume the transilient mode in the body aspect—that you are an eternal spirit—there is no time pressure and you feel like playing, one act of which might be paddling toward your goal. Transilience in the mind aspect—where the world is mysterious and wondrous—has a similar playful quality. You might be wondering what is around the next corner, and thus be curious enough to paddle there.

"The transilient assumption in the spirit aspect, gives the feeling of being one with the paddle, the water, and the goal. By letting it all flow together, you feel naturally like paddling toward your goal.

"The transilient assumption in the emotion aspect— the transilient good in the present—opens you to an experience of the perfection and love of the universe with its force for good flowing through it. With all this transilience available just by shifting your assumptions, you can see there is no problem at all with lack of energy in the calm space. Try it and see what happens."

Explorer feels a little overwhelmed from receiving such a long lesson, but he has followed it with surprising clarity, and is ready to try it. He moves naturally into the Question-Answer Process, and asks himself, "What transilient assumption should I try first?"

The answer comes that, first, he needs to clear a little agitation. When he asks what is generating the agitation, he finds he is assuming that this is too new and hard. He will never be able to do it right. He changes that by remembering that his main talent as a human being is his ability to make assumptions, so he assumes he could do it quite well. That calms him, and he repeats the question about which transilient assumption to use. He decides to try each one briefly to reassure himself that he can, in fact, make each one true, if he so chooses.

Explorer finds that he can make each of the first three: He can be in empathy with everything; he can relax in the safe knowing that he has all eternity to reach his goal; and he can get into the thrill of being in a mysterious and wondrous world. But when he comes to the fourth one, he finds he has a barrier. He cannot easily assume transilient good to exist and to be more ancient, real, and powerful than the physical world. Explorer's childhood religious training has left him with some scars. His current concepts of God are, that either he does not exist, or he does exist but is not powerfully present in our everyday lives, or else God is very judgmental and punishing.

Space-Holder points out that Explorer is in charge of having created his experience of God. He can alter that experience through making new assumptions.

That statement amazes Explorer. He mulls it over for awhile, then goes into the Question-Answer Process to discover his old assumptions about God, and to shift to some new ones. He hopes that through the new assumptions he can create a more nurturing experience of transilient good from God. His process is as follows:

What is my assumption that generates a judgmental feeling from God?

That if God exists, he has a preconceived idea of what is good and what I am supposed to do and be.

What is a new assumption that would calm this?

God and I are co-creators of the good; it is neither that God has a pre-set plan—which under this new assumption would be too autocratic on God's part— nor that I have all the say about what is good — which would be too willful on my part. God and I meet as equals in a community of spirit. We each share our truth about facts and feelings and come up with a consensus decision about what to designate as my future good.

"Wow, did that really come from me?" exclaimed Explorer. "Am I really a partner with God?" Space-Holder smiles and says, "Try it—test it—ask yourself some more. You'll either confirm your partnership or change it."

This new perspective gives Explorer a wonderful feeling of energy and joy. He thanks Space-Holder and moves toward his boat, delighted and desiring to paddle toward his goal.

TABLE IV

Symptoms from Over-Running an Assumption

The conditions which result from using an assumption beyond the time when it is effective.

ASPECTS OF ME	OVERRUN ASSUMPTIONS	SYMPTOMS RESULTING FROM OVERRUN	ASSUMPTION TO MAKE FOR HEALING
MIND	Knowing	*Dogmatic*	In Mystery
	In Mystery	*In a Battered Reality*	Knowing
SPIRIT	Uniquely Individual	*Isolated and Numb*	In Empathy & Kinship
	In Empathy & Kinship	*Having Fuzzy Ego Boundaries*	Uniquely Individual
BODY	Striving	*Defensively Compulsive*	Relaxing in Safety
	Relaxing in Safety	*Unable to Sustain an Intention*	Striving
EMOTIONS	In a Good Story	*In a Shattered Good Story*	Just Being Now
	Just Being Now	*Drifting Without Goals*	In a Good Story

Chapter 5

Burnout from an Over-Running Desire for the Goal

Several weeks later, Space-Holder comes to check on his pupil, and is dismayed to find Explorer showing obvious signs of burn-out. His temper is short; he looks hollowed-eyed; he is relying on addicting substances to enable him to function at all.

"What on earth happened to you?" asks Space-Holder.

Explorer moans, "I've lost it! I was in great shape, paddling along making great progress. I set my goals for the future and was hell-bent on making them happen. But then, I started to get exhausted (sob)....and there is so much to be done that is vitally important to do. I can't get enough others to help me, and the future good which I saw is slipping out of my grasp. I have tried and tried to make a difference in the world and the world is still an awful mess. I can't quit or give up trying as long as I have any strength to go on . . . or I'll feel like I'm losing my integrity and my dedication. I've done my best—more than seemed possible—but it didn't help. Now I am as big a mess as the rest of the world. Maybe I'm just not good enough or diligent enough or smart enough (sob). Help me!"

"Sure thing," says Space-Holder, trying to get Explorer calmed down and centered enough to listen to his new lesson. "You were correct in setting goals of future good but you got off the track in your technique of working toward them. Simmer down—get sober—and I'll explain what to do. Space-Holder reaches for a thermos and pours Explorer a cup of his favorite strong tea. Explorer mumbles his thanks and rests on the bank.

"Your basic mistake", he continues, "was to use the energy of your desire to fulfill the goals and give you motivation to work. As we talked about (in Chapter 3) the other day, using the energy of desire is as debilitating a method as using fear and agitated energy to get you going. You learned quickly to recognize agitated energy, and you realized that it created a poor atmosphere in which to live and work. The error here—in using desire—is sneakier, but just as damaging in the long run."

Explorer rises to his own defense. "What I was doing was good! Why wouldn't I desire to do it? Why shouldn't I desire that glorious vision of future good? It's so wonderful and I think everyone would appreciate it if it came to pass."

Space-Holder cuts him off. "You are mixing up two different activities. One is setting the goal. The other is striving toward it. Those are totally different and need to be handled in different ways.

"First of all, remember how you originally set the goal."

Explorer thinks back. "I remember wanting to do good in the world. I felt love welling up in me and I looked around to see what I could do to make things better. I had a vision of what the future good would look like. I talked it over with God—in my inner dialogue—and with my friends. We all got consensus about the vision being good and worth working toward."

Space-Holder points out that this process of envisioning the goal and coming to consensus does not involve physically striving in the world. "It was done while you were sitting back and telling your truth as you became clear about it. It was a form of sitting around a campfire telling stories. This is a totally different activity from physically doing the work to create it," he says.

Space-Holder adds that it is appropriate and necessary to set goals. "We need to have the currently designated good on our priority list, so when we have some time and energy to spare, we know what to do with it. It lets us know what direction we are headed in. Otherwise we would all just be drifting and going in random directions which wouldn't be in alignment with God or the force for good in the universe. The problem is not that we set a goal which we didn't know how to accomplish. The problem lies in the source of the energy to actually work toward the goal.

"We have to desire the goal when we are setting it, or we would not know what to aim for. We can feel our desire for it whenever we are checking to see its current direction. Desire is like a magnetic compass—it gives the direction of good. But to try to use desire-for-the-good as a source of energy for paddling toward it—this gets us into no end of trouble.

"Striving toward a specific future good—for which you have a detailed concept and strong desire to attain—is excessively transfixed. Three of the four aspects are in the structuring mode—in Table III: striving, knowing, in a specific good story. The only transilient left is empathy, which is not by itself sufficient to give the energy to function effectively. In fact the empathy tends to trap you further into the excessively transfixed state because you feel the pain and suffering of others which you are trying to heal in your vision of future good.

"The solution to your problem is to move from three transfixed assumptions—and one transilient—in Table III, to two of each. If we are stipulating that this situation calls for striving—the transfixed assumption in the body aspect—then there are two ways to achieve the balance. We can drop the knowing or drop the desiring.

"Dropping the knowing is the only effective way to be striving and desiring at the same time. If your goal is making the world better it's necessary to give up trying to be a know-it-all about how that will look or happen. If you change from being a know-it-all to the transilient in the mind aspect—by assuming you are in empathy in a mysterious, wondrous world—then you are able to be nurturing to mankind in a general way without thinking you know exactly what is best for them. This is useful to do in intimate family relationships—or in small supportive groups—but it doesn't enable you to be effective and appropriately defending of yourself in larger groups and organizations.

"The second way to achieve the two-to-two balance is to give up desiring a specific good goal. You can intellectually remember what the goal is without actively desiring it. This is a more effective way of striving toward a specific goal because it includes being able to assume the world is knowable. In this solution the transilient energy comes from empathy in the spirit aspect—mixed with transilient good in the present moment from the emotions aspect.

"This gives you the energy you need to go toward the goal. You only do as much as you have the energy for at the moment. Being in empathy with God—rather than with the pain and suffering which you are trying to heal—enables you to work appropriately at your own pace—with energy from within and without getting trapped in the overwhelming enormity of the job.

"Remember what Mother Teresa said when she was asked if she didn't become discouraged in her work with the destitute and dying: 'God has not called me to be successful. He has called me to be faithful.' (Time Magazine) Mother Teresa and her nuns work diligently toward their intellectually-remembered goal of helping the destitute but they do not feel desire for that goal—they feel desire for their experience of God which they do in the transilient good of the eternal now."

Space-Holder suggests that Explorer center himself, let go of his desire for a future physical good, and do a little Question-Answer Process to determine what aspects of this lesson he is still reluctant to accept.

Explorer takes a deep breath and settles down to look at the situation. His first question is:

What do I do with this desire I feel pulling at me if I am not supposed to use its energy when I am striving?

His answer came up immediately from the spiritual lessons he had learned in the past.

I am to assume I already have the future desired good. If I assume I already have it—that puts a cap or patch over it so I don't desire it so much any more. In a surprised tone he exclaimed, "This is what affirmations are for! I used to think they were just a kind of magical incantation that was supposed to bring about the previously chosen good some-how. Now I see that an affirmation simply puts a person in the most effective position to create the desired good—or to let it show up—and be able to notice its showing up."

Explorer continued with his next question.

If I give up desiring the future good, won't I forget what my goal is?

That is why they keep telling us in goal-setting seminars to write down the goals—so we won't forget them.

How do I get the energy to strive for a goal I no longer particularly desire?

I know what Space-Holder would say: "Use the energy created by the transilient assumptions."

All right, if I were going to do that, what transilient assumptions would I make?

If I am going to be striving and knowing—both transfixed from body and mind aspects—then the transilience will have to come from the spirit and emotions aspects—by having empathy and by just being with the experience of transilient good in the eternal now.

Explorer looks up and says he knew a lot of good people who were allergic to such religious ideas, and would refuse to make an end run by using such transilient experiences. "This makes me feel like I'm cheating—taking unfair advantage by using them," says Explorer. He closes his eyes and the next question comes:

Is it unfair to use assumptions about transilient good in a situation where others refuse to believe in them?

Others who tend to be narrow-minded might think so but they'd have to admit the possible reality of transilient good in order to voice a complaint. If they're allergic to even the idea of it they probably won't say much—and if they do you can ignore them by 'canceling their vote.' In the land of the blind—the one-eyed man is king. That is just the way it is. You don't have to be obnoxious by rubbing it in that they are blind—but that doesn't mean you should not use your own abilities.

It has hurt me in the past when someone denied the reality of the transilient good that I believed in. Won't it be as hurtful to them—in their different beliefs—if I assert my reality in their presence.

Transilient good is so 'spacey' that they can easily call it whimsical or crazy and thereby ignore it. It's not nearly so rigid as their denial of its reality that hurt me—though I imagine it will make some of them sick to their stomachs. But the proof of the pudding is in the eating. If this is a useful way for me to live—and it keeps me from burn-out and addictions—then I think I have a right to use it.

Why did I end up in addictions to handle my burn-out?

I was trying to get immediate gratification of my desires—and especially desired substances that numbed my pain or gave me more temporary energy to put into my overly transfixed desire for the good goal.

I worry that I won't get to the goal as quickly if I don't use a desire for the goal to motivate me. Wouldn't I get there quicker using desire?

"Dummy—did you get anywhere by burning yourself out?" one part of Explorer joshed himself. "Don't be a silly unrealistic overly perfectionistic ninny!"

How do I handle the pain and suffering I see in the world?

Don't be in empathy with them anymore than it is useful to be. Put up your boundaries by being in your unique individual mode when observing the problems and pain in the world.

Isn't that too hard and callused?

Not if it is more functional.

Will mankind ever get healed?

The future isn't fixed. Maybe it will and maybe it won't. Doing the best you can does not mean burning yourself out. When you are burned-out and sick you are more of a liability than an asset to the world.

I am afraid to do it this new way. What is the inaccurate assumption I have that is generating this fear?

There is some pre-set standard for giving my heart and soul to life—a standard I won't measure up to.

What is my new assumption that will clear the fearful agitation?

God has given me this life so I can figure out how a human being works best. The more I experiment and try new things the more I will learn.

If I learn this new way—and it works well—am I not responsible to teach others?

Only those within hearing who show an interest in listening—and even then mostly as an aid in teaching it more to myself.

Space-Holder finishes writing down what Explorer has been saying and asks, "Are you willing to try it the new way—using only transilient energy when striving and not using your desire for future good in the world?

Explorer isn't sure he'll really be able to do that right away, but notices that he is much calmer. He feels he will still need some resting time to heal from his burn-out. Explorer says, "I'll try to keep myself clear about it. Will you be around the next day or two in case I want to talk some more about it?"

Space-Holder smiles and nods.

(Tables III and IV are repeated on the following pages for convenience.)

TABLE III

**Pairs of Transfixing and Transilient
Assumptions about Myself**

("I am . . .)

ASPECTS OF ME	TRANSFIXING ASSUMPTIONS	TRANSILIENT ASSUMPTIONS
MIND	*. . . Knowing"*	*. . . In Mystery"*
	I live in a knowable world where it's possible to figure out anything.	I live in a mysterious, wondrous universe, unknowable in its entirety.
SPIRIT	*. . . Uniquely Individual"*	*. . . In Empathy & Kinship"*
	I am a unique, separate, individual, viable being.	I am one with all, in empathy and kinship with all creation.
BODY	*. . . Striving"*	*. . . Relaxing in Safety"*
	I need to strive hard to survive and succeed in this physical world.	I am relaxed and trust that my existence is supported by the eternal universe.
EMOTIONS	*. . . In a Good Story"*	*. . . Just Being Now"*
	I focus on my vision of the future good which is better than what is now.	All the good that exists is present in this moment and available if I open to it.

45

TABLE IV

Symptoms from Over-Running an Assumption

The conditions which result from using an assumption beyond the time when it is effective.

ASPECTS OF ME	OVERRUN ASSUMPTIONS	SYMPTOMS RESULTING FROM OVERRUN	ASSUMPTION TO MAKE FOR HEALING
MIND	Knowing	*Dogmatic*	In Mystery
	In Mystery	*In a Battered Reality*	Knowing
SPIRIT	Uniquely Individual	*Isolated and Numb*	In Empathy & Kinship
	In Empathy & Kinship	*Having Fuzzy Ego Boundaries*	Uniquely Individual
BODY	Striving	*Defensively Compulsive*	Relaxing in Safety
	Relaxing in Safety	*Unable to Sustain an Intention*	Striving
EMOTIONS	In a Good Story	*In a Shattered Good Story*	Just Being Now
	Just Being Now	*Drifting Without Goals*	In a Good Story

Chapter 6

Emotional Storms Arise en Route, Raining Agitation

Space-Holder returns the next day to find Explorer waiting for him and obviously in some agitation.

Explorer is embarrassed to be experiencing agitation again, but Space-Holder points out that everyone has frequent episodes of agitation, especially when first adjusting their 'internal computer' to be operating from more accurate assumptions. "It is a little like needing to take a bath everyday or to routinely brush one's teeth. Just because we keep getting dirty again doesn't mean we are living wrong. We just need to realize we need daily maintenance of our assumptions as much as we do of our body," says Space-Holder.

He suggests that Explorer tidy up his inner condition using the Question-Answer Process. Explorer moves over to a comfortable spot on a flat rock and proceeds.

What is the emotional feeling going on in me?

Space-Holder interjects, "The agitated energy can usually be identified as fear, sadness or anger." Explorer continues,

This one is definitely fear.

What is the assumption I've made about reality that's generating this fearful agitation?

That I'm doing it all wrong.

Space-Holder suggests that Explorer ask himself how old he was when he first decided to assume, "What I am doing is all wrong," and that he notice what event has just happened which results in his making that assumption.

Explorer closes his eyes again and lets himself float back in time. He asks himself if he had that assumption as a teenager, or earlier at age ten or age five or whenever. Explorer believes in reincarnation, and if it seemed necessary, he could go to a previous incarnation when he had made that assumption. This time, however, the answer comes that it happened in his present lifetime, at age six.

What had just happened?

I see myself with goop all over my hands from having tried and failed to create something with wet pottery clay. I don't want the goop on my hands, and I feel bad that I tried and couldn't make—yes I couldn't make the pot I wanted to. I feel like I must be basically a person who does things all wrong.

Space-Holder points out that Explorer's six-year old self is the one who has made the assumption, and so his six-year old self is the only one who can change it. Adult Explorer can act as a coach, guru or therapist to his six-year old self, to try to enlighten and guide him into making a new and more functional assumption.

Adult Explorer speaks to his six-year-old self: "Young One you are a wonderful kid. I am yourself grown-up so you can see we made it this far. But the basic assumption you made about feeling 'What I am doing is all wrong,' is limiting my life now and causing me miserable agitation. I can see why you made it. You were discouraged by the potting fiasco and you didn't know any better than to make such a limiting assumption. Would you be willing to change it to something like 'I am a wonderful playful being and I just had an interesting unsuccessful experience trying to make a pot'?"

Six-year old Explorer listens intently and catches the glinting light from his grown-up self's spirit. It sparks in him the memory of who he is, a divine Child of God, who finds himself in this giant sand box we call life. He realizes that "playing" more accurately describes his activities, and since he knows he is basically wonderful, he doesn't have to take his failure to make the pot so seriously.

Explorer tells Space-Holder that this exercise has cleared that agitation, but now an even deeper one is coming up. Space-Holder tells him not to be discouraged. It doesn't mean that there's an infinite number of agitations. There will probably be a reasonable number, which can be worked on each day. It will be neither overwhelming nor arduous. He should just tidy up the agitations for each day, so he will have considerable time the rest of the day to spend in nurturing calm and peace.

Explorer buckles down, and asks himself what assumption is generating this new deeper agitation. "It's emotion is dread," he says. "The old assumption that is generating the dread is, 'Who I am is basically a total screw-up'.

Explorer remembers Space-Holder's instructions, and asks how old he was when he made that assumption. He answers himself,

> I'm in my mother before birth—in the first months of my fetal life—and I'm causing my pregnant mother to continually vomit. My conclusion is that if I am practically killing my very own mother—I must be a total screw-up and should never have been born.
>
> *What new assumption about my fetal self can I make instead.*

Mom volunteered for this in order to give me physical life. She knew it might involve misery and risk and I should be grateful to her for it and thank her instead of condemning myself for existing or causing her misery.

Explorer feels relief by thanking his mother, and his feelings open up in an expanded inner atmosphere to live in that day. He asks himself if there is any further tidying up he needs to do right then. The answer he gets is another question.

How much really quality space do you want to have today?

Explorer got his own answer, "Lots!"

His next question is,

OK, then ask yourself what new assumption you can make now that will result in your feeling that way.

The answer comes,

To assume I am really a wonderful person.

"That feels much better," chortles Explorer. With his renewed spirit, he happily goes off to paddle toward his present goal.

Chapter 7

Evil Pirates Attack the Boat

Space-Holder, nears the creek, hears a great ruckus and comes running to the bank. He soon spots Explorer being attacked by a band of pirates, each in a little boat. They wave swords of vicious accusations and throw barbed spears of insults at Explorer. Several manage to ram his boat, badly agitating him.

When he sees Space-Holder on shore, Explorer yells for help. "Tell me how to handle this!" he shouts.

Space-Holder calls out asking Explorer what he is doing, dealing with those strangers who have such negative attitudes. While doing his best to fend them off, Explorer calls back that he had to travel past their encampment to get to his goal. As soon as they saw him, they set out to attack.

Space-Holder watches the action, pointing out that Explorer could have taken a more evasive route and avoided them altogether, but now that he is within reach of their barbs, he will have to handle the situation before he can get away. He calls out that the only barbed spears that have any effect on Explorer are those that find some vulnerable part of him. Therefore, he can use this encounter as an exercise in learning where his vulnerable parts are, and how to toughen them up. "Just notice the assumption you have that leaves you open to each specific attack," calls Space-Holder.

Explorer is fairly frantic by now, but takes the advice to heart. He strains to sense exactly what he is experiencing. First he feels a jab from a spear labeled, "You are a bad person and always do everything all wrong." He knows he isn't a bad person, so he easily fends off that part. But the part about doing it all wrong re-stimulates his old assumption that he had replaced only yesterday. The new one is still not very strong or automatic, but he remembers it, so he counters with the truth: "For years I thought I was basically doing it all wrong, but I don't believe that anymore. I am a playful spirit who experiments and tries things. Get away with your negative energy."

Amazingly, that chases the pirates off for a time, but the next day they return, disguised as legitimate boatmen coming to do business with Explorer. Through this ruse they got closer in, and then accuse Explorer of illegal business practices and falsely blame him for smuggling; they claim he said libelous things that had never been uttered. Explorer is beside himself trying to fend them off, because he is still confused about whether he is supposed to view them as good guys who were a little neurotic, or bad guys to be shunned. Explorer wants to give the pirates every opportunity to prove themselves as being fine fellows after all, so he keeps trying to get them to agree to the truth that their lying behavior is wrong. He keeps trying to get them to say that they are sorry for being so wrong, mean and wounding. He thinks he owes them, as fellow human beings, divine children of God, every chance to become truthful and remorseful, and then redeemed.

Space-Holder finally has to step in and interrupt. Explorer is rapidly becoming a weak, exhausted, immobilized victim. "Stand up for yourself," Space-Holder shouts. "You will never get agreement from these lying, verbally-battering pirates. They are bad guys and have no integrity. Quit giving them more chances. Take charge of the situation and distance yourself until you can no longer feel the barbs of their false accusations. They have transgressed beyond where you can afford to honor them. Turn them over to God for their chance for future healing, and protect yourself!"

Explorer hears these words, and notices how strangely comforting they are. For a moment, he wavers, thinking that maybe he should continue to offer these tormenters the truth about themselves as best he knows it. But that impulse doesn't last long. He takes note of how much damage the pirates have done to him. His boat of assumptions about reality has several holes in it's hull from their sharp lies. Explorer is so weak and wounded that he really has no choice but to defend himself or go under. With a last burst of energy, he maneuvers out of reach of the pirates and makes for shore near where Space-Holder is standing.

He gets out of the boat, takes a deep breath, and asks himself what assumption he is making that had allowed these pirates to nearly do him in. It comes to him that he had been taught as a child that a good person never turned his back on anyone. Everyone had to be saved and healed before anyone had a right to feel joy. Then he recalls a phrase from C. S. Lewis's book, "The Great Divorce"[2] if we let pity for those who refuse joy, to keep us from our own joy, we will let a 'Dog-in-the-Manger' be the tyrant of the universe. What lurks behind that merciful-sounding principle (that all must be saved before any are saved) is the demand of the loveless and the self-imprisoned that they should be allowed to blackmail the universe: that until they consent to be happy (on their own terms) no one else shall taste joy: that theirs should be the final power: that Hell should be able to veto heaven."

Explorer had once memorized that passage, and is glad that he remembers it so it can again ring in his ears. This is certainly a situation in which it applies. He shares his memories with Space-Holder who encourages him to keep on thinking.

Explorer sits down on the bank and wonders aloud how, in the future, he can distinguish between those people he should shun and those deserving of his help. He recalls stories of drowning people being so frantically clinging that they caused their rescuer to drown with them. How can he tell, before he gets so wounded, who is appropriate to try and help? Who should be labeled as evil and shunned? To whom should he show compassion and help?

Space-Holder speaks up offering a suggestion about what criterion to use. "We know that a person who has inaccurate assumptions about who they are (such as 'I am bad but I will try to be nice so people will like me'), will behave very erratically, trying to compensate for their dysfunctional assumptions. Imagine a person who assumes he is basically unworthy and who tries very hard to be seen as worthy. For example, others could sense a person's insincerity and his unctuous attempts at flattery. They would view him as lacking in integrity, and would reject him. He might retaliate against this rejection with brutality in an attempt not to be reminded that basically he's assuming his unworthiness. His brutality is a knee-jerk reaction, an automatic unthinking defense.

"We really can't say this is deliberately malicious, yet it's very damaging to others. And its source is an inaccurate assumption for which the person himself is responsible. He could change it if he chose to do so. Granted, the person would require a lot of clear thinking and self-examination to notice his inaccurate assumption (such as, 'I am basically unworthy') and still more clear thinking to know the possibility of replacing it with an accurate one (such as, 'I am basically good and wonderful, and I occasionally make mistakes'). Further granted, it's not likely he'll be able to do this clear thinking unless he has the right kind of support. Still, it seems to me, that it is time in our cultural development to assign responsibility to the person for his own assumptions and his knee-jerk responses that follow. People will never learn that they are responsible for their own assumptions unless we start giving them straight feedback and holding them accountable."

Space-Holder turns and asks Explorer, "Would this criterion work in distinguishing whom to help vs. whom to see as evil: Worthy people clearly have integrity down to their good divine core?"

Explorer thinks about it. Certainly those pirates would flunk such an integrity test. No one, who was assuming that he was basically good and worthy, would behave in such a dastardly way. He notes that he would certainly have more nurturing interactions with people if he limited his contacts to those with integrity. He wonders if he has a right to avoid the bad guys. Explorer asks Space-Holder, "Who will help the bad guys wise-up about their assumptions if I don't interact with them and call them on it?."

Space-Holder reminds Explorer that he didn't have to save the world single-handedly. Even if no human would interact with a bad guy, he could always turn to God, if he were only willing. "There are some stubbornly evil people out there," said Space-Holder, "and they are way beyond what us ordinary folk can do to be helpful and not be excessively damaged ourselves. Leave them to heaven."

"Compare the example in evolution," he continues. "Alligators as reptiles are much less evolved than mammals such as rabbits or humans. But alligators are much stronger and would win in any unarmed combat. The thing to remember is that as mammals we need to take responsibility for running the zoo!"

Explorer laughs and rises up slowly, realizing that he is becoming stiff from sitting so long. He puts his arm around Space-Holder's shoulder and thanks him for the insights.

After that, Explorer steers carefully clear of pirate dens, and defends himself deftly if a stray pirate happens to come near. Sometimes he wonders if he really deserves to have such a nurturing life, only playing with good guys, but then he remembers who he is—a most worthy and deserving child of God—and he relaxes into his good fortune.

Chapter 8

Excessive Zeal Turns Away Listeners

Some weeks later, Space-Holder finds Explorer in a new quandary. Every time he tries to get some enthusiasm from others for his new, wonderful way of life, he notices that he is being too zealous and assertive. People seem to find him overly enthusiastic and draining to listen to. They increasingly find excuses to leave his company quickly.

He paddles over to where Space-Holder is standing, to ask what he could do about the unfortunate effect he is having on people.

Space-Holder pulls out his charts and blackboard again. This time, he shows Explorer how the transfixing and transilient assumptions, that he has learned earlier, can be combined in a balanced way, so that at any one time he will have some structure in his approach (transfixed) and some openness and energy (transilient). By having some of each, he can avoid being either too solidly pushy or, on the other hand, too "spacey". He shows Explorer the chart of the six possible combinations.

"If you start with the idea," continues Space-Holder, "that there are four holistic aspects (mind, body, emotions, and spirit) and that we are going to stipulate that two of the four aspects shall be in the transfixing mode and the other two in the transilient mode, then there are six and only six possible combinations. As you can see from Table V each of the six combinations—called roles—has been assigned a number—one through six—in no particular order. Each

TABLE V

Six Balanced Roles in Life

ROLE NUMBERS AND NAMES	TRANSFIXING ASSUMPTIONS (Structured)	TRANSILIENT ASSUMPTIONS (Energizing)
1: HEALER— MYTH MAKER	Knowing + In a Good Story	In Kinship + Relaxing in Safety
2: THRILL SEEKER— SPORTSMAN	Striving + A Unique Individual	In Mystery + Just Being Now
3: CRAFTSMAN— SCIENTIST	Knowing + Striving	In Kinship + Just Being Now
4: ROMANTIC— ARTIST	A Unique Individual + In a Good Story	In Mystery + Relaxing in Safety
5: NURTURER— PROTECTOR	Striving + In a Good Story	In Mystery + In Kinship
6: THEORETICIAN— DETECTIVE	Knowing + A Unique Individual	Relaxing in Safety + Just Being Now

role has also been assigned a name chosen to symbolize a function often performed in that role.

"For example," says Space-Holder, "Role #6—the Detective-Theoretician—is the one you have been using to do the Question-Answer Process. In this role you're transfixedly assuming that you are a unique separate individual being—one who can know about the world. You are using the energy from the transilient assumptions that you are a relaxed eternal spiritual being who exists in present time and experiences the questions and answers floating up spontaneously from realms of transilient good. If you think back to how you felt while doing the Question-Answer Process, you had enough structure and not too much and you had enough energy and not too much. There was a balance in it. You could calmly walk through the steps of the process without being too pushy or dogmatic—which would have been too transfixed—or too fuzzy or confused—which would have been too transilient.

"Let me walk you through the other five roles first and then we'll see if we can analyze what you have been doing that resulted in your being compulsively pushy and over zealous with your friends about these new principles.

"I like to think of the six roles as three pairs. Within each pair every aspect that is transfixed in one becomes transilient in the other. Similarly what is transilient in one becomes transfixed in the other. Thus within each pair, one role is the exact opposite of the other.

"The opposite of Role 6 is Role 5—the Nurturer-Protector. In this role the transfixing assumptions are that one has to strive and work hard physically—the body aspect—to create good in the world—the emotions aspect. The transilient assumptions are that one is in empathy with everyone—the spirit aspect—and in mystery in a wondrous world—mind aspect. Thus when operating in this role, a person is taking his cue about what is good from what the others want and doing one's best to supply it in a nurturing, protecting, loving way.

"It's my observation that most people have one pair of roles that they use most often and are most comfortable in. They can exercise all the various transfixed and transilient assumptions by just alternating between the two roles in the pair. What they are missing if they do not exercise any of the other four roles' combinations is the opportunity to use the most appropriate role for the particular job at hand. Thus for example, if one was taking care of children in Role 5 and had a career in research using Role 6's detective-theoretician talents, when it came time to do the income taxes or write an arduous paper neither Role 5 nor 6 are as suitable as the Craftsman-Scientist Role 3.

"Role 3 assumes that the world is knowable and that one has to strive to succeed or survive—transfixed in mind and body. Its transilient assumptions are being in empathy—spirit aspect—and in the present moment with the experience of transilient good—emotions aspect. This is the role I was describing in an earlier lesson that Mother Teresa and her nuns use to nurse the destitute and dying in Calcutta. They experience loving God and God loving them in the present moment of transilient good. They are not attached to the physical future good of a whole world healed nor to taking care of each other. That is their intellectually stated goal but they are not attached to a desire for attaining it or they would burnout. And heaven knows while doing my income taxes, only an experience of God loving me can carry me through without my soul being in pain from agitated energy!

"Notice the difference between using Role 5 to take care of a family in a nurturing way versus using Role 3 to do it in an efficient way. Maybe it would be best to use each one some of the time—but if I had to be a child in a family being taken care of in only one role—I think I would prefer the love in Role 5 to the efficiency of Role 3.

"Proceeding with the pair in which Role 3 occurs, its opposite is Role 4—the Romantic-Artist. In this role, the transfixed assumptions are that one is a unique separate individual with a unique perception and experience of the

60

good. The transilient assumptions here are that one is a relaxed eternal being living in a mysterious and wondrous world. This is the role in which we want a virtuoso performer to play for us—to play from his heart in Role 4—even though we know that he had to practice long hours in Role 3 to learn his craft.

"The last pair of Roles—Numbers 1 and 2 —are also opposites of each other. Role 2 is very valuable when we are in a dangerous situation demanding our striving physically for our own unique individual survival—body and spirit aspects in transfixed mode. It's the role we resort to in order to defend ourselves. It can also be used for fun in sports or thrill-seeking adventures. If used during a time of inward focus, it is a meditation role—using the striving to focus our attention on our unique physical experience of breathing. The transilient assumptions are that one is in a mysterious world—mind aspect—in which one experiences transilient good—emotions aspect. This transilient experience of the divine in the present moment is what is meant by the saying 'There are no atheists in foxholes.'

"The opposite of Role 2 is Role 1—the Healer-Myth Maker. This is the role we are in when sitting around the camp fire in the evening telling the stories and myths of our tribe which give collective meaning to our lives. In a very real sense our relationship is such a story—telling the truth about goodness and the goodness about truth. The goodness about truth is that we can sense it—truth—by an experience of agitation indicating untruth—and a calmness which indicates that our assumption is true. The truth about goodness is that our stories about goodness are a multiplicity—not a singularity. Our good stories are not the same for everyone—contrasting with the laws of physics which are the same for everyone. There is no single good story out there that we are trying to uncover and clarify in the manner we uncover and clarify the laws of physics. Our good stories are created out of an empathy with God and other humans—all of us co-creating them—and coming to consensus about them while in a state of community and empathy with each other.

"The ideal about the six roles is that each of us should be able to do any of the six roles with competence using whichever role is most appropriate to the job at hand.

"This is quite different from the ideal held by Western Culture which tells us that we are supposed to be all four transfixed assumptions all at once. It states that we are supposed to have strong individual egos—striving physically—while knowing what is going on—and living in a shared story about what is good in the physical world in the future and that we're all working toward. If you have any doubt about that being our Western ideal, notice that we expect our Presidential candidates to debate each other on TV while demonstrating all four transfixed assumptions all at once. No wonder our politicians become burned out. No wonder we are not able to elect more effective leaders.

"Scott Peck advocates—in his book *A Different Drum*—that the Presidential nominees pre-select their cabinet-to-be and all of them run as a group that experiences community with each other and makes consensus decisions. Then we could have nominees who would be expert in each role—and they could demonstrate their prowess against opponents in an arena of activity specific for each role. Then maybe we could have a more functional government.

"I probably shouldn't try to speak about any culture but my own—but I have the idea that Eastern Cultures have all four transilients at once as an ideal. Obviously, that is too spacey to be very functional.

"Changing the cultural ideal to one of having a balance of transilient and transfixing assumptions at any given time may sound less efficient than four transfixed ones all at once but it would work much better. In the same way, democracy works better than a fascist state though the fascist trains may run on time more often. Democracy may be less efficient but has much more viable space in which human beings can live and thrive. The same can be said for balanced roles.

"This has been a rather long-winded lecture but I think it will be useful. Let's try to use it to analyze what you were doing wrong," concludes Space-Holder.

Explorer cannot believe that he has been doing it wrong this time. He heatedly points out that he had only wanted others to learn this new way of living so they could also live in this wonderful way.

Space-Holder asks him whether he is seeking agreement from people about his new beliefs. Explorer acknowledges that he has been feeling a little lonesome, and is trying to get his friends and acquaintances to become as enthusiastic about these new principles as he is.

Space-Holder asks Explorer to do the Question-Answer Process to check and see in how many of the four holistic aspects he is assuming the transfixing assumption.

Explorer settles down asks himself: "Am I assuming I am a knowing being?" He answers: "Yes—definitely. I know these principles and concepts and I know they work well and I want others to know them too."

Explorer continues: "Am I designating a future good in the physical world that is better than the present?" He answers himself: "Yes—definitely. I am picturing everyone being able to know and to use these principles and have their lives work much better than they do in the present."

Explorer begins to suspect that he might be making too many transfixing assumptions, but he bravely presses on. He asks himself about the next one: "Am I striving to succeed or am I being relaxed in having all eternity to accomplish whatever good I have in mind?" He admits to himself that he has been seriously striving. It has seemed so urgent to get others to know and understand the principles. "I didn't think I should passively wait for them to learn."

He presses on to the fourth aspect: "Am I being a unique separate individual or am I in empathy?" He answers himself: "When I was lonely I was separate. When I sensed that others' lives would work better if they used these principles I was in empathy. I would score myself half and half on this one. But I'll admit that the more resistance I met in other people the more of a striving unique individual I became about it."

"I can see that I stand guilty as accused," continues Explorer. "I was being excessively transfixed in my approach to teaching and enrolling people in these principles. What can I do about it?" Explorer asks his coach.

Space-Holder suggests that he look at what comes up in his experience in answer to that question, and to continue in his own process.

Explorer says, "I think I need to separate my goals and only try to accomplish one at a time. If I'm lonesome I should use an empathy role—if I'm trying to teach I should use a knowing and striving role. Role 3 would cover both those—if I were willing to let go of desiring the good outcome and just focus on the teaching process. Then all I'm missing is this wonderful feeling of seeing something I love and desire so much that it moves me to my socks."

Space-Holder points out that Explorer's love and desire feeling sounds like a Role 4 experience of being in love. "If you are trying to teach theory—best done in Role 3—then don't expect to move people with your eloquence," says Space-Holder. "Get your love from God in the transilient good in Role 3. If you want to be eloquent and move people with your unique virtuosity—let them be in the mystery with you in Role 4 which is no place for teaching theory. If you want to teach about goodness—Role 1 would be your best bet but in that role you can't be striving or a unique individual without becoming over-zealous pushy and self-righteous. Just relax around the camp fire and share your story as one among many—not pushing it down anyone else's throat. If someone asks you to teach theory it is soon enough to move to a Role 3."

Explorer can see the wisdom of all this, but admits that his desire for having it all at once is hard to give up. He resolves to get more of his joy from transilient good, rather than trying to save the world single-handedly.

Chapter 9

Futile Attempts to Paddle with the Sail

A few weeks later, Space-Holder came to find Explorer again, to see how he was coming along. To his surprise, he finds him in a bizarre condition, flailing around trying to use the sail as a paddle while mired down in an area of marsh grass near the shore. He asks Explorer what on earth was going on.

Explorer readily stops his futile paddling and says, "It hasn't been working very well anyway. I only tried it as an experiment. I just wasn't getting anywhere when I was using the paddle. I thought I would try something different. You said I should experiment. Using the sail seemed like a good idea at the time—it has a bigger surface area than the paddle so I thought it might move me on better. Unfortunately, I found out how awkward it is—trying with a sail whose mast is longer than I am tall, and whose sheet fills with more water than I have the muscles to move. When I realized that problem, I decided to try making only one big stroke per hour, and resting in between. That is actually the tempo I had been using with the paddle recently—one stroke per hour—and resting in between. I was trying to get more transilient energy during the rest times."

Space-Holder smiles beneficently and says, "It looks like it's time for sharing some principles about using the appropriate role for the task at hand. Why don't you come ashore. There isn't much marsh grass between you and this bank." While Explorer navigates the boat and ties it up, Space-Holder gets out his charts and blackboard again, including one showing six balanced roles, each having half transilient assumptions and half transfixed ones (Table V).

Explorer looks around for flat rock to sit on, but Space-Holder looks up and says, "Look, it's beginning to rain. Let's sit for awhile over here on the bank and use your boat as a shelter. Just lift it out of the water, and turn it upside down, with one side propped up by these two poles. We will be warm and dry while we discuss which role to use in various life situations."

Explorer does as his coach suggests, and soon they are comfortable and dry. Space-Holder positions the chart between them under the cover of the boat.

TABLE V

The Six Balanced Roles in Life

ROLE NUMBERS AND NAMES	TRANSFIXING ASSUMPTIONS (Structured)	TRANSILIENT ASSUMPTIONS (Energizing)
1: HEALER— MYTH MAKER	Knowing + In a Good Story	In Kinship + Relaxing in Safety
2: THRILL SEEKER— SPORTSMAN	Striving + A Unique Individual	In Mystery + Just Being Now
3: CRAFTSMAN— SCIENTIST	Knowing + Striving	In Kinship + Just Being Now
4: ROMANTIC— ARTIST	A Unique Individual + In a Good Story	In Mystery + Relaxing in Safety
5: NURTURER— PROTECTOR	Striving + In a Good Story	In Mystery + In Kinship
6: THEORETICIAN— DETECTIVE	Knowing + A Unique Individual	Relaxing in Safety + Just Being Now

"The six roles are mutually exclusive," says Space-Holder, "you can only be in one at a time. The names are only suggestions—each role can be used for many different activities. It's kind of like the boat—you can use it for floating on the river or for shelter here on shore. Looking at the roles for example, you can use Role 2, Thrill Seeker/Sportsman, to fight if you find yourself in a battle, or to meditate by striving to focus attention on a physical sensation, like breathing. You select a particular role by choosing either the transfixed or transilient qualities that you want to utilize. Ideally, everyone should be able to use any of the six roles, as the situation demands. In practice, people usually find that two of the roles fit their nature best and are most comfortable to be in for most of the time.

"The criterion for selection in your present situation," he says, "is to determine which role's assumptions work best. In order to figure this out, you must examine the situation you're in at the moment, and your designated goal. Which role's attributes 'work best' is defined as those which best achieve the goal. Tell me what situation you're in and what goal you are working toward."

Explorer reviews his recent experiment. "I was on my way to Nurturing Landing to pick up supplies when I became bogged down in an area that was heavy with reeds and marsh grass. The water was thick with them and they impeded my progress. I remembered what you said about only using transilient energy to paddle, so I didn't get into a panic of agitated energy and I didn't become burned-out from an intense desire to get past the reeds and marsh grass. I tried to get more transilient energy by relaxing, by going into empathy with the marsh grass, and by staying in the mystery and wonder of it.

"I was really enjoying the experience until I realized I wasn't getting anywhere. It looked like I'd be stuck in the marsh grass forever if I didn't do something different. That's when I got the idea of using the sail as a paddle. When you came along, I was just deciding to quit the experiment as it wasn't working very well."

Space-Holder nods and asks Explorer to check out how many transilient assumptions he had been using all at once.

Explorer counts three of the four being transilient—relaxing, being in empathy, and being in mystery. The only transfixed one is that of desiring the goal of reaching Nurturing Landing in good time.

Space-Holder points out that the way to approach the problem is to decide which of the assumptions to make transfixed and which transilient. "When this is done, you have automatically pinpointed the role that will work best. It's not going to help much," he says, "to shift into knowing—you could know all there was to know about marsh grass and still be stuck in it. It also will not help you in moving past the marsh grass, to shift into being a unique individual on a quest for adventure—being stuck in marsh grass would be very boring for an adventurer. The only way to move yourself out of the marsh grass is to put some striving muscle into paddling. This requires shifting from relaxing in the safety of eternity to striving with the paddle."

Space-Holder emphasizes that striving was a necessary part of any role that was going to work in moving him out of being mired down in marsh grass. Knowing this fact reduces the options from six roles down to the three roles which all included striving. "Look at each of these three roles," says Space-Holder, "and see if you can predict which one would work best in your present circumstance."

Explorer looks at the table to compare the three striving roles. "Role 2," he begins, "with its defensive unique individual stance, doesn't seem warranted since the marsh grass is not actually attacking me. The choice between the other two striving roles—3 and 5—is between 'knowing' in Role 3's Craftsman-Scientist or 'desiring the future good' of being out of the marsh grass in Role 5, the Nurturer-Protector. In Role 5, I could be nurturing to myself, but I would be in mystery and not know what I was doing."

"That," points out Space-Holder, "sounds like what you were trying to do with all those transilient assumptions:

trying to nurture yourself without knowing what you were doing. Do you think that your trying to nurture yourself made you too tempted to relax and not strive in your paddling?"

Explorer looks at it objectively, and says, "I suppose so. I can see that going into an organized efficient Role 3, with striving and knowing what I am doing, is going to work best to get me out of the marsh grass. But I don't understand how to do that without still having a 'desire' to get out of the marsh grass, which would result in too many transfixed assumptions."

Space-Holder reminds Explorer of the lesson in Chapter 4—that he could be in Role 3 and still remember what the goal was. "A person needs to be in touch with his desire earlier, when he is setting a goal, but can let go of the desire later when he is working and striving toward it," explains Space-Holder. "Just remember the goal intellectually. That's why it helps to write down goals."

"What should I desire instead?" asks Explorer.

"Desire the transilience in this role," declares Space-Holder. "Desire to be in empathy with the transilient good in the present moment. Desire to be in alignment with the force for good in the universe, whose power acts in the now, not in the imagined future. Desire to love God and to be supported by God's love in the striving toward your remembered goal."

"So I don't really have a choice of roles?" Explorer asks plaintively.

"Not if you want to accomplish your goal of moving out of your stuck place in the marsh grass," says Space-Holder. "The way you were doing it is like trying to nurture your way while walking into the dentist's office or doing the income taxes. At some point, you either bite the bullet and do it, or it never gets done."

"I thought I had more choice about it than that," complains Explorer. "I thought I could use these principles to make my life really good."

"Not unless you want to stay stuck in marsh grass all your life," replies Space-Holder. "You could live blissfully stuck in the marsh grass if you chose, but it would be hard to ignore all those other boats on the open water with their paddlers frisking about here and there and getting to their various destinations."

"Yes, I see what you mean," says Explorer. "It's just hard to convince myself that I really have to buckle down and do the work to get out of this stuck place. How come I was so unlucky as to get stuck in this marsh grass? Did I do something bad, and this is my karmic punishment? Was I stupid and not watching where I was going? Did God plunk me down in the middle of the marsh grass to teach me a lesson? How should I view this situation?"

"What would the Role 3 attitude be?" asks Space-Holder, "since that is the role you have decided would work best here."

"I guess Role 3 would not be paying any attention to the past good story of how I got there, or the future good story of what good it would do me to have been there. I would just be paying attention to the job, in the now, striving and paddling, to get through the marsh grass with as much knowledge as I can muster. Using the sail as a paddle was not very clever."

Explorer continues complaining: "How do I get over feeling guilty for getting mired down in this stuff?"

"What assumption would calm the guilt?" asks Space-Holder. "It seems like something in the realm of transilient good, such as 'God loves me'. Experiment with some transilient good assumptions until you find the one that works best, and then use it."

Explorer thinks about it for a time, listening to the last of the rain drops resonate on the boat hull above them. He carefully narrows his mental focus. He lets go of the past where he might have been guilty of an error. He lets go of the future where the vision of his desired good lay. He focuses his attention on the glint of light he senses coming from his immediate inner experience. He keeps focusing on the glint until his awareness is narrowed to where the glint fills his whole field of vision. Then he lets himself go into the light. He has shifted into Role 6, Detective-Theoretician, so he still has knowing, along with being a unique individual, trying to figure his unique way out of this problem. He recalls his goal of finding words for a transilient assumption which he could love and desire. He then slides into the Question-Answer Process, asking "What assumption, if I made it, would enable me to love and feel loved in this present moment?"

The answer comes: "God is with me." He shares this with Space-Holder, explaining that in his use of the word "God" he means the universal force for good that loves him and whom he loves as a child loves a parent.

"Try it on for size," Space-Holder says. "If you assume 'God is with me', do you feel both energized and knowing what you love and desire?"

Explorer closes his eyes and silently makes a strong assumption that God was with him. "Yes, of course," he says. "It works like a charm."

"Do you feel energized and centered enough to go out there and exert your muscles, striving to paddle through the marsh grass?" asks Space-Holder.

"I do, if I can stay centered in this assumption," declares Explorer.

Space-Holder notes that the rain had stopped and they could turn the boat right side up again. He points to their different use of the boat being like the different use of the balanced roles. "Sometimes you can use a role one way, sometimes another way, depending on your goal. For instance, Role 3 could be used to attain a spiritual goal, with the choice of which particular striving activity being secondary," he intones.

Once they had turned the boat right-side up and put it back in the marsh-grass-filled water, Explorer climbs aboard, waves his thanks and starts paddling. At first, he finds he has to use energy to focus on his intention to make his new assumption. He reassures himself that after a while it will become a habit that he can use whenever he chooses. Right now, he can obtain the extra energy he needs by experiencing the lift it gives his spirit to actually be moving successfully toward his goal of getting out of the marsh grass.

After a few minutes, he notices that he has a passing gloomy thought: "Will it really be possible to assume 'God is with me' when I am doing those dreadful income taxes?" However, he quickly notices that the question is about the future, and he is supposed to be focused only on the present, so he decides to worry about the income taxes when the time comes. "Ho-ho-ho," he chortles, "this stuff works!" He paddles off grinning from ear to ear.

Chapter 10

Subversive Crew Member Making Holes in the Hull

Explorer's life has been working so well that he acquires a little bigger boat, and joins with a few other explorers to form a group as close-knit as a family. He had wanted to share his good life and knows that close relationships with others give him an opportunity for greater fulfillment.

They were paddling along, successfully arriving at one goal after another, until one day Explorer suddenly has a sinking feeling and notices that the boat was filling up fast with water. He bails quickly, but the water keeps rising again. The water is murky and he can't see the bottom of the boat to find out what is wrong. He lets out a yell for his old coach, Space-Holder, who he's sure has been tracking his progress, and heads for the nearest shore to dock his disabled craft.

Space-Holder comes sauntering along; he is enjoying the summer sunshine, and wonders if he can teach the buzzing bees to do minuets with each other. He has just about decided it is too hard to get the bees' attention, much less to motivate them into thinking a dance was better than a simple zigzag course from the hive to the flower and back. He is glad to have the chance to talk to Explorer again. Their communication level seems to enable him to make more of a difference in the world than his experiments with the bees, not that the bees wouldn't be fun. They were such lively energetic creatures.

As he comes strolling up to where the disabled boat is sitting low in the water, he finds Explorer and his family group sitting around gloomy and grumpy, moaning about their failure to keep their boat hull free of multiple leaks. Space-Holder greets Explorer and is introduced to the group. After some small talk, he asks if anyone has any theories about what has gone wrong. Everyone tries to speak at once, each accusing the others of causing the problem. "What a lot of sound and fury," exclaims Space-Holder. "If you will all just quiet down for a while I think I can sort this thing out.

"The boat hull is your mutual structure of reality, constructed of what each of you assumes to be true. It is stable and has enough integrity to float and keep the creek water out as long as all of you stick to the truth. My detective work here will be to figure out which of you has been playing foot-loose and fancy-free with the truth. Each of you ask yourselves about who in the family is dedicated to truth, and who thinks it is all right to lie, exaggerate, disparage, or conceal the truth. Explorer, you be the spokesperson for the family group and tell me your perceptions."

Explorer moves off a little way from the others to try and get his head clear. Space-Holder joins him, and waits as Explorer sorts through his thoughts. The more Explorer tries to do this, the more agitated he becomes. Finally, he confesses to his old coach that he cannot tell what is true any more. He says he has thoughts that one of his family members had become a traitor, and was consorting with pirates. However, when he confronted the potential traitor, that person denied it, and was indignant and incensed that Explorer could think such unkind thoughts of him. The more that Explorer found out about the situation, the more he saw signs of traitorous activity, and the louder the potential traitor insisted he was innocent of any wrongdoing.

"Now I am so confused," moans Explorer, "I don't know what to believe. The potential traitor says he loves and supports me and the family, but he acts in ways that are devastating to my feelings of self-worth. He claims he is only defending himself against my attacks on his worthiness. He claims that he's not doing anything wrong when he is away, but will not give me adequate facts so that I know where he's been. He says that if I love him, I should trust him. I know I am an emotional mess and have been very defensive about his accusing me of being at fault for doubting him. Maybe I can no longer perceive truth accurately, and I should just give in and go along with what he says as true, if only to keep the peace. I don't know what I should do. I am so confused. I used to think I was so clear about the truth that I would never be confused again, and yet here I am again back in the soup!"

Space-Holder puts his arm around Explorer's shoulders and comforts him. "I have just the input for your problem. Relax a little and listen while I explain the situation you're in. It's been called a Battered Reality Syndrome.

Explorer nods, "If my boat hull is my structure of reality, calling this a 'battered reality' really fits. This confusion about what's true—it's just like my boat hull having holes that I can't find but are leaking like a sieve. I don't know where the water is coming in, but I know I'm sinking fast."

Space-Holder sets up some new charts and begins to explain: "There are four kinds of lies that verbal batterers can use. As I describe each kind of lie, you do some Question-Answer Process about whether the potential traitor is guilty of that kind.

"The first kind of lie is one that you have already described him doing: Withholding data or facts about where he has been and with whom he has been consorting. This is lying by *concealing the truth* so that his family members can't get enough facts to be able to know the truth with certainty."

Explorer immediately says, "He certainly is guilty of that. He claims that he doesn't have to tell me the facts because he deserves his privacy. Is that a valid point?"

Space-Holder instructs Explorer to do a bit of the Question-Answer Process by asking himself that question.

Explorer closes his eyes and formulates his question as clearly as he can:

Is it valid for a family member to have privacy about where he goes and whom he goes with?

I don't know.

What comes up after the "I don't know?"

I experience a lot of confusing agitation.

Space-Holder reminds Explorer to ask what assumption about reality he has that is generating the agitation.

Explorer asks himself, and comes up with: "In order to have the nurturing that a family can give, I have to be in empathy with them at all times and at all costs, and this makes me vulnerable to being hurt by them."

Space-Holder suggests that Explorer look for a new assumption that he could make instead, one that would calm the agitation.

Explorer says, "If a potential traitor has the right to privacy and thus to hold himself emotionally distant from me, then I also have the same right to privacy and emotional distance, and that would enable me to defend myself in the situation." Explorer continued in the Question-Answer Process:

Have I been appropriately defending myself?

No, or I would not be such a wounded mess.

What is my reluctance to defending myself in this situation, when I did fine at repelling the pirates' attack?

In a family situation, I think I am always supposed to be open and in empathy, never closed and operating as a unique individual.

When did I decide that, and what had just happened?

When I was 8 years old, and saw how hurt my family members were when one of us was closed and hard in the unique individual mode. I remember one time when my dog died, and my father was embarrassed by my crying, and harshly told me that I was a big sissy, and that I should stop it. That really hurt, and I vowed that I would never be closed and hard with any of my family members. I have not been able to do that always, but I always think I should try to do so. People in families are intimate and open in order to be able to nurture each other. I decided that they are too tender and vulnerable for any of them to go into hard unique individual modes with each other.

What did I expect my family members to do when I got stressed and I inadvertently went into an irritable and harsh unique individual mode for a short time?

I expected them to defend themselves as appropriate and discount my outburst, pretty much cancelling my vote for the moment. They could see I was under stress and would forgive my temporary aberration.

Why have I not done that in this situation with a potential traitor?

Because I can't quite believe he's a traitor. If I knew he were a traitor for sure, I could take appropriate defensive action.

Why have I not been able to be clear about whether he is a traitor or not?

Because maybe he isn't a traitor, and this whole thing is really my sickness about not being able to trust people.

How can I be sure?

Like anything I am certain of, I have to assume it is true.

How can I get clear on which is true?

I don't know.

What comes up after the "I don't know" experience?

Huge agitation.

What assumption do I have that is generating this agitation?

I assume that if there is anything wrong in my family, it is my fault and I'm the only one who can change and fix it.

When did I decide that?

When I was a child, and no one else in the family seemed willing to change to make anything better and more loving in the family.

What would be a new calming assumption?

Sometimes it is my fault and sometimes it is someone else's fault. In the latter case, I should take appropriate defensive action.

How do I know whether it is my fault or their fault?

First I do detective work and find out as many facts as possible. Then, I look at the facts objectively and make my best guess as to what is really true. Then, I go with my best guess and assume it's true. I do this for a prolonged period and obtain more data from my experience of how it works during that period.

Eventually, if it still seems to not be working, I can re-evaluate the new data and try a different assumption. For instance, if I decided this potential traitor is really at fault, and throw him out of my family, and then it happens again and again, until I have little if any family left, then maybe I will try assuming it is my sickness about not being able to trust, and I will do psychotherapy or something to work on it.

Space-Holder interjects a comment here: "Try checking out the other three types of lies, and see if the potential traitor is guilty of any of those. People who are willing to lie in one way, will often think it is all right to lie in other ways too."

Explorer asks about what the next type of lie is.

Space-Holder says, "Lies about facts are the most obvious. If your detective work uncovers proof that he was really at a bar when he said he was at work, or that he was really with one person when he said he was with another, this shows the potential traitor has at best, a low level of integrity about lying.

Explorer searches his memory for such a situation, but could only come up with circumstantial evidence. The potential traitor had been too good at concealing things to let Explorer have such proof of prevarication. "What is another kind of lie?" he asks.

Space-Holder points to another type of lie on the chart. "In this type of lie, he accurately states the facts of what happened, but he lies about who caused it to happen. He lies about who is at fault or to blame."

Explorer notices that Potential Traitor did tend to blame him and other people for things. If he had an accident, he immediately yelled at someone else that it was their fault for having distracted him or not been nice enough to him. That certainly gave a clear indication of Potential Traitor's lack of integrity. "What is the fourth type of lie?" asks Explorer.

Space-Holder replies, "This is the kind of lie a person tells about another person's self-worth, by calling them bad names or casting doubt about their basic goodness."

Explorer remembers numerous times when Potential Traitor called people unkind names. "He calls bad drivers by terrible names, and he once called me a nosy troublemaker when I complained about his mysterious behavior," recalled Explorer. "I can see that Potential Traitor is definitely the kind of person that is not scrupulous about telling the truth." Without any suggestion, he returns to the Question-Answer Process:

> *Is this evidence enough for me to justify kicking him out of my family?*
>
> It seems a very harsh action to take on such limited data. Maybe I could get conjoint counseling with Potential Traitor, and get the truth clear between us.

Space-Holder interjected a warning: "You can't expect to get agreement about truth from verbal batterers. Lying is their biggest weapon in attempting to manipulate and control the situation. They're not going to give up this weapon with your gentle plea for clarity in a counseling situation. Even if you threaten to throw them out of your family, at least emotionally, they probably won't believe you'll really do it until long after they have been shunned. If you let them, they'll try to keep counseling sessions going forever without coming clean about the truth.

"You have to take decisive action by distancing from them. The only thing that gets the attention of verbal batterers is the loss of their victim—you. When they realize they can no longer wound their victim, sometimes—not often—they'll shape up. Distance yourself from them sufficiently so that they can't any longer make holes in the boat hull of your assumptions about truth and reality. If you ever let them close again, they will have to be exceptionally scrupulous about truth. One little sign of confusion on your part should immediately result in your pushing them away again. You cannot handle this situation with kindness and gentleness. Acknowledge that the very fabric of your life is threatened—your boat is really sinking—and shift into a strongly defensive Role 2."

Explorer says that he knows how to do a strongly defensive Role 2, with its unique and striving individualism. He just couldn't believe he needed to do it. He resumes his Question-Answer Process:

How could I be so stupid as to let a traitor into my family?

I did not know he was a traitor at the time I let him in.

Why could I not discern that he was a traitor?

Before he could answer, Space-Holder injects another comment: "Liars are very good at what they do. No one should expect themselves to be able to spot a liar right away. Liars often spend years developing a convincing charming facade. The only way to spot a liar is to watch his behavior.

Explorer experiences agitating fear.

What is my inaccurate assumption generating this fear?

I should be able to spot a liar, and if I don't, there is something the matter with my ability to perceive reality.

What is my new calming assumption?

I forgive myself for not being able to spot a clever liar, and only fault myself if I don't take decisive action to shun him after I have observed his behavior being destructive.

How can I be sure that this family member really is a traitor?

I can't get total proof. I only know that someone put holes in my boat hull and it wasn't me. Potential Traitor is the obvious candidate. While I can't prove it, and he won't give me the data to prove it—or any other agreement that he has done wrong—I still have my power and ability as a human being to assume the truth and thereby create my solid boat hull of reality. It will hold nicely as long as I keep Potential Traitor away from it. Keeping liars away from the boat hull of my reality and truth

continued on page 84 . . .

TABLE VI

Four Types of Lies Causing a Battered Reality

TYPE OF LIE USED BY THE BATTERING PERSON	DESCRIPTION OF THE LIE	PATHOLOGICAL CONCLUSIONS BY THE BATTERED PERSON
FALSEHOOD	Incorrect description of what actually happened.	"I am wrong"
FALSE BLAME	Incorrect attribution of the cause of what actually happened.	"I am to blame"
PUT-DOWNS	Incorrect description of the other person's essential worthiness. Name-calling. Hateful, vicious and sarcastic tones.	"I am worthless"
EVASIONS	Inadequate feedback about what is true; deliberately fogging the issue; silence; absences.	"I am crazy"

TABLE VI

Four Types of Lies (continued)

TYPE OF LIE USED BY THE BATTERING PERSON	HEALING ASSUMPTIONS
FALSEHOOD	You are deliberately lying to me. I have to wall myself off against you and not let my concepts of reality be affected by what you say. I cancel your vote.
FALSE BLAME	You are 100% responsible for any of your actions. If you did it, you are to blame. If your life did not turn out right, you did not do it right. I put the responsibility for your life on you, and for my life on me.
PUT-DOWNS	You are being a bad person for saying that I am unworthy. As long as I am honest and have basic integrity, I am me and that is not a matter of right or wrong. Being me is the most solid and worthy thing I know.
EVASIONS	You are deliberately trying to prevent me from having a clear experience of what is true, and that is a very mean thing to do. I will assume to be true whatever my current best data tells me is true, and I will act on those assumptions. If you continue to evade me, we can no longer have a partnership of equals, and I have to distance myself from you.

is definitely my responsibility and I'll use whatever means I have to, to put Potential Traitor at a sufficient distance that he can't damage me any more.

How do I shift out of my strong defensive stance in Role 2, into one of the empathy roles with my other family members?

I need to be safe. I need to know that Potential Traitor can't reach me any more. That I'm safe from his lies and manipulations and put-downs and subterfuges. Once I know I'm safe, I can easily shift into empathy roles with my nurturing family members.

How can I keep from repeating this mistake?

I think I can spot the next liar quicker, but I'll forgive myself if I don't notice him until I see his damaging behavior.

Why is there not more public outcry about the dangers of such verbally battering liars?

They have strong PR—public relations—but we are catching on to their games quicker. The truth shall make us free!

Chapter 11

Boat in Storm Shattered by Rocks of Traumatic Events

Some months later, in dead of winter, a big storm on the creek blows Explorer's boat onto sharp rocks, smashing a big hole in the boat hull, and killing one of Explorer's loved ones.

Space-Holder rushes to the area to assist in the rescue operations. He finds Explorer bruised and bloody, clinging to his boat that is still on the sharp rocks that pierced the hull. His loved one's body having been removed by the coroner, Explorer remains in a state of emotional shock.

Space-Holder instructs Explorer to leave the boat where it is for the moment, and to join him on shore for some mental first aid. Explorer climbs out of his boat, and clambers over the rocks to the sheltered place on the shore where Space-Holder is setting up his usual charts and chalkboard.

Space-Holder gives a brief description of the problem before having Explorer begin an intensive Question-Answer Process for centering and clearing. "What you have here," begins Space-Holder, "is a shattered good story. Your old good story did not have space in it to handle the death of your loved one. When your boat crashed into the harsh sharp truth of events which your good story didn't include as possible, the good story of your boat hull was shattered.

"The process of healing requires two phases: The first phase is coming to grips with the reality of the harsh truth. In the second phase you create a new good story. This second phase takes a long time—many months or years. The first phase can be accomplished fairly quickly if there is enough focused support. Since the old good story is shattered, none of the three roles with future good in them are usable. This eliminates half of the six roles for weeks or months, until the beginning of a new good story grows. The remaining three roles all have "being with the experience of transilient good" in them. This experience of transilient good is the 'dry dock' that the shattered hull of good story needs to be put in for repair. It will stabilize and support the person during the first phase where the harsh reality is faced. At that point, it seems to the person there is no good anytime in the future. The experience of transilient good becomes the base from which the new good story will grow."

Explorer numbly absorbs this data and expresses his gratitude to Space-Holder for being with him in this traumatic time. His mind feels too boggled to think about the problem by himself, and if left alone to deal with it, he would have stayed stuck in a numb fog for a long time.

Space-Holder says it is important to have another person present to facilitate coming to grips with the harsh reality. He settles Explorer comfortably, and gives him a warm cup of tea to sip. Then he quietly lets Explorer share his thoughts and feelings. Space-Holder writes down what Explorer says, as he goes through his long process, because it will be useful to Explorer to read later when he would otherwise have a hard time remembering the steps of his healing process.

At first, Explorer just says whatever comes to his mind. Later, Space-Holder reminds him to find a question, and notice the answer, and assuming that to be true, to find his next question—the Question-Answer Process.

Explorer gratefully accepts the cup of tea, and is most appreciative of having another person's attention focused on the problem. It seems so overwhelming. How can he ever come to grips with the enormity of the horror? His feelings recoil time and again, refusing to admit that the harsh facts could be true. He keeps repeating the same phrases over and over: "This cannot be true. It is impossible. My loved one was alive and well and vibrant only a few hours ago. How is it possible he could be gone so quickly? It feels like the whole fabric of my life is torn to shreds. If this is true, nothing makes sense any more. There is no goodness anywhere in a universe where this could happen. My heart feels like it is being torn right out of my chest. I can hardly breathe. It feels like a giant has just stepped on me and crushed me totally."

Space-Holder gently asks, "Can you find a question?"

Explorer replies:

Why did this awful thing happen to me who am a good person?

Maybe I did something wrong in piloting the boat. If only I had listened more closely to the storm warnings and paddled harder to get to a safe-harbor, then this dreadful thing would not have happened. And if only the other crew members had been willing to paddle harder, I would have chosen to go to the safe harbor; that means my other crew members share my blame. I can't do everything myself.

Am I being too critical of the other crew members in blaming them also?

Yes. It wasn't their fault.

Was it my fault?

I am torn: If I assume it was my fault, then I have to acknowledge that I am bad and defective where I could have been better. This would cancel my assumption that I was a good person doing the best I could. I can't think of any realistic way I could have done it better. And I know that it almost always works best to assume I'm a good person doing the best I can. Therefore, assuming that I am at fault doesn't seem to be helpful.

"But the alternative seems even worse: If none of us humans were at fault, then we are out of control of our lives, vulnerable to horrible accidents in an uncaring universe. There is no force for good strong enough to overcome the random chaos. I refuse to think of the universe as evil—I know absolutely that assuming such a thing doesn't work. But thinking that the force for good is weaker than the tendency toward chaos is very scary to me."

Space-Holder interjects a reminder: "Fear comes from the agitated energy of an inaccurate assumption. What assumption about reality do you have that is generating this fear?"

Explorer asks himself that question, and reports what comes up next for him: "The force for good is not basically in charge of everything."

When did I decide to assume that?

Today, when I confronted the loss of my old good story.

What could I assume instead that would be calming?

If I could believe it, it would be that the force for good was active in this event in some way—that it had some good purpose which I can't see at the moment.

What is my barrier to assuming this?

I can't believe that a real force for good would cause such an awful event. I can't believe there is anything good enough to be worth the amount of pain I am experiencing.

What would enable me to believe that?

To believe that the good we are heading toward is even more wonderful than I previously thought— even more magnificent and incredibly beautiful.

What is my barrier to believing that?

When I was a child, my parents believed in a world of limited good: I gave up my child-like experience of the wonderfulness and glory of life in order to fit in to their world view. I was afraid that if I did not fit in, they would toss me to the wolves or see me as a total fool who would never be good enough. It felt like I couldn't have survived in my parental family if I had had such a glorious view of goodness in the universe. I can see that I had to accept their limiting belief then, but once I got to be an independent adult, I could have changed back to my expanded view of goodness.

Why didn't I?

Inertia. This is the first time I have encountered events so traumatic that I have had to confront the limitations of this belief.

Will my child-self accept my new incredibly expanded belief now?

Yes. The old belief was shattered with the smashed good story. It may be that I am only grabbing at straws, but I have to try. It seems like the only thing available to hang onto that enables life to make sense. If it doesn't work, I am no worse off than before because all feels lost in my present mode anyway.

What is my first child-like step in this new belief?

That I am so humbled and so much less than I thought I was, in the face of this incredibly expanded concept of the force for good in the world. I'm not bad. I'm just small.

Will I eventually grow, or will I always be this small?

It feels like I have already grown a little just by being willing to take this first step.

I feel like asking the force-for-good whether I will continue to grow.

(Explorer pauses.) It answers me: "Yes, my child; in this fertile field which you call painful loss, you will grow beyond your wildest dreams. Be true to yourself, and love me as any good being loves the force for good, and all will be well. Let your growth unfold as a natural process in the quiet places of your everyday life. As your newly expanded ideas of good become more stabilized, let them expand again, little by little, revealing the truth about mystery. Now you have moved toward my truth, rather than your parents' truth, and you and I together will move even further beyond what has limited your experience of the glory of living."

Am I talking to a real being or another part of me?

Which assumption works best?

I feel so small, it is better for me at present to view this experience as another being. Later, perhaps I will be big enough to view it as part of me. In the meantime, I can experience this personified force for good as a being within me that offers me energy, aliveness, love, and wise answers. This being and I are co-creators of my personal good. I discover what I desire as a future good, and this force for good is the source of the energy to create it. This being and I need to be in consensus and alignment with each other for my good to manifest. We can create this community of spirit within me by my taking time to meditate, dialogue and do the Question-Answer Process.

Are there any pitfalls in this process?

Only if my psychic circuits are not in shape to take on this much energy without burning out. I suppose

I may blow a little fuse from time to time; that I can handle and repair afterward.

Would or could it ever blow my circuits totally, leaving me a babbling idiot?

There is risk in anything in life, but I am a sturdy Explorer who usually keeps his boat hull of assumptions about reality in good repair, so it seems like it is worth the risk for me to embark on this new spiritual journey.

It comes to my mind to ask: What about my loved one who died? What is or was his relationship to this force for good?

It is agitating for me to believe that he was cut short in his life by a random violent force over which he had no control.

What is my inaccurate assumption which is generating this agitation?

That he had no choice about dying.

What assumption would calm me?

That he could and did choose to allow his life to end at this time, out of good intention.

What possible good intention could he have had?

He might have felt that a more pressing spiritual job could exist to be done than he might be doing in his present earthly incarnation, and he allowed himself to be available to make such a transition at this time. I can't know another person's spiritual path as well as he knows it for himself, so I probably won't be totally clear about what this pressing spiritual business might be. It's enough to calm me to assume that he knows, allowed himself to die and wasn't just a victim of random chaos."

Space-Holder speaks up at this point: "Even if you assume that he allowed himself to make his transition at this point, you will still feel the pain of your loss of the bond with him until you do a little adjusting of your wound. Recognize and acknowledge the painfulness of your severed bond. Some people view it as a psychic umbilical cord that has been cut, and the end still attached to you is bleeding and in pain. It is important to bring this bleeding end back into yourself. Some people re-attach it to their own heart, or head, or belly button, or somewhere; or just open up and re-absorb it totally into themselves. Do what ever feels right for you."

Explorer gingerly feels the painful stump of his severed bond. He asks Space-Holder: "Won't I lose all contact psychically with my loved one if I don't keep this bond hanging out there, even if it is painful?

Space-Holder explains that after a person makes his transition into an after-life state, he creates a new kind of bond with his loved ones. This new bond is of a different quality, is not based in having any physical contact, and is more easily created when the old physical bond is not in so much pain.

Explorer asks himself:

Where would it work best for me to put this painful bleeding bond back into myself?

I don't want to ground it in any one place because my relationship with my loved one was on more than one level. I think I will attach it in the blood within my heart that goes to all parts of my body.

Explorer continues: I feel better for now, but I know the pain will come back whenever I am reminded of my loss during my daily life.

How do I handle it when the pain comes back?

The most important thing is centering in transilient good in the now, peeling away any stuck pieces of the old good story, so I can operate in my daily life without tripping into painful pits all the time. I guess I just have to do this with each activity that reminds me that my loved one is physically gone. I suppose that will be a slow painful process but I think I have a good handle on how to do it now.

"When can I get my boat back in the water?" asks Explorer.

"When it holds out the creek water and doesn't sink," replies Space-Holder. "Test it from time to time as the new good story grows to fill in the shattered hole. It may take many months before it is seaworthy again. Give it time. In the meantime, keep yourself fit by doing your daily routine on shore. And give your other family crew members room to go through their own processes about this loss. Give them support in feeling their feelings, and be gentle about suggesting they find a more calming assumption after they have been in an agitated state for awhile. People adjust to these things at their own pace, and they know the appropriate pace for themselves better than anyone else."

Explorer gave Space-Holder a big hug, and went off to set up the new routine of his family group on shore. He was still in pain, but at least he was functional, and no longer felt totally stuck and immobilized in his sorrow.

Chapter 12

Numb Heart from Traumatic Events

Explorer seeks out Space-Holder many months after the traumatic loss of his loved one. He is back on a fairly even keel, but he wants some guidance about his inner spiritual life. Still numb from his loss, he is looking for some advice about how to open his heart again. He wants to be able to feel love and joy again, rather than just a numb neutrality. He feels that something in his spirit has died with his loved one, and he wants to know if there is a way to revitalize it.

He finds Space-Holder softly playing a homemade flute, tuning it to the sounds of the life of the meadow in which he is sitting under a shady tree. He welcomes Explorer and they settle down for a good talk about Explorer's situation.

Space-Holder listens to Explorer's review of his troubles, then suggests that he begin with some Question-Answer Process about the problem of his heart trying to open again.

Explorer closes his eyes and senses the feelings in his heart. "It feels tightly closed, tense, frightened," he says.

"Would you like to ask yourself what assumption you have that is generating the fear?" asks Space-Holder.

Explorer calms his fear enough to ask himself the question. What comes up as an answer is the idea that death would always claim anyone he loved, if not now, then later. "No one ever got out of this life alive. If I open my heart to love again, I know for sure I'm going to get hurt by it sometime in the future. The pain is so awful, it just doesn't seem worth it to open up and love again."

"That certainly sounds like a very powerful limiting assumption," chuckles Space-Holder. "No wonder you're having trouble opening up. Can you think of any alternative new assumption that would be calming?"

Explorer mulls this over. "It seems like a crazy way to have made the universe, to have the spirit of love be so oppressed by death and the blackness of loss in life. It seems like such a no-win situation."

"Maybe that's not the way the universe really is," Space-Holder suggests. "Your assuming that view is agitating you, which would indicate that it isn't true. What is a different view you could assume experimentally?"

Explorer thinks over the various views he had read or heard about, but none of them seemed appealing or calming. Next, he sinks deeper into his experience, and asks what question would be useful to him. What comes up is as follows:

How do I get in touch with and experience the vitalizing force for good in the universe?

(Thinking deeper yet, trying to open to a meaningful answer, he feels the intense aching and longing in his heart.)

What is my heart longing for?

The image I get is of joining, of reaching out and linking in a way that feels wonderfully warm and enlivening.

What is it that I am longing to link with?

It isn't a 'what'; it is a 'who'.

Who is it that I am longing to link with?

The person I love.

Whom do I love?

The face of my deceased loved one comes up.

Are you the spirit of my dead loved one?

'Yes, I am with you always, here in your heart.' Explorer feels a brief rush of warm feelings of love which are quickly followed by doubts.

How do I know you are real and not just a figment of my imagination? asks Explorer.

The spirit answers, 'The proof of the pudding is in the eating. Try relating to me as if I were real, and see whether the effect in your life is beneficial or not.'

Explorer begins a dialogue in earnest with the spirit of his deceased loved one:

Where are you?

'I am where a person goes when one dies. It has more dimensions and fluidity in some ways than earth-plane existence, and less in other ways, so it is hard for me to describe it in earth-language. For myself, I like to call it the Bright World. The colors of the grass, trees, flowers, and sky are so much brighter and more vivid here. This world seems more real and solid than earth-plane. It seems more eternal. But I remember how real and solid those molecules feel when one is in a physical body. Therefore, I don't expect you to completely believe me in this. Just use the possibility that what I am saying is true. It will work as a springboard for developing a new calming assumption that will enable your heart to open to loving and being loved.'

If only I knew that you were real, that you as a spirit really exist and that I could look forward to being with you again after I too am safely dead, then my heart could rise in joy. I would know that nothing could be lost

forever. I would be willing to wait to be together again.
But how can I be certain of this?

'Remember the principle of how a person is certain of anything.'

Explorer thinks for a minute, and remembers that the only way to be certain of anything is to assume it to be certainly true. He remembers the rule that no amount of data will cause us to change from one assumption to another, from uncertainty to certainty. Data can be used as a springboard but the data cannot push or force anyone into making a new assumption. Each of us, for himself, has to take the action and make the new assumption in order to be certain of anything.

So you could materialize and spend all your time with me,
and that still wouldn't be enough data to make me certain
that you are still alive in spirit, and always will be. No
matter how much data I have, I still have to make the
shift in my assumptions for me to be certain. And, simi-
larly, I'm always able to make the new assumption no
matter how little data I have about the truth of it. I can
make an assumption with no data supporting it at all. I
make the assumption in order to experiment with using it
and see if it works.

The spirit of his loved one seemed to positively beam. It says,

"Now that you have the principle clearly in mind, you can
ask specific questions about your reluctance to assume
with certainty that I am real and alive in this Bright
World."

Explorer asks himself:

What assumption do I have that is making me reluctant to assume that this experience of my loved one is real?

I have no proof and I would need proof to convince others that my belief in this is not crazy.

Space-Holder joins in the conversation at this point. He knows what has gone on because Explorer has been speaking his inner experiences as they unfolded. Space-Holder points out that the proof Explorer was seeking ran into the same problem as data had earlier. No amount of proof could force another person to change his mind about whether Explorer was crazy. "One person would and another wouldn't. So some people will agree with you already," he says. "Some will shift their assumption to align with your new belief, and some will never shift no matter how much data you accrue. Therefore, you may as well assume it with the data you have now."

Explorer continues his Question-Answer Process:

What will happen if some people think I'm crazy?

Some of them will be gracious enough to allow me to have a different view without bad feelings. Others will say disparaging remarks about my sanity. I guess I could just cancel their vote, and put distance enough between us that I am not annoyed by them.

How do I feel about becoming so distant from those who neither align or make space for me to have a different view?

I feel a sense of loss, of peeling off some old relationships that I have kept for a sense of security and continuity.

What is my inaccurate assumption generating this feeling of loss?

That there was anything to lose—that the security they offered was real when it couldn't help with the pain of losing my loved one.

So, what other reluctance do I have in making this new assumption that the spirit of my deceased loved one is real?

It will require other shifts in my belief system—a sort of domino effect. If this one falls, the one next to it gets knocked over, and so on down the line.

What is the first old belief it bumps up against?

That when I die, it will be the end, a black nothingness in contrast to the Bright World my loved one describes.

What new belief would fit here?

That I too am an eternal spirit who existed before I was born and will continue to exist through and beyond the transition I call death.

What old belief does that one bump into?

If I count on that and base my life on it, what if it turns out not to be true and I have to endure that too as a loss?

Explorer jokes that if he really didn't exist any more after his own death, then he wouldn't mind. There would be nothing there to experience the loss. But that argument did not bring calm, so he looks further.

Explorer begins to see that he need never experience the agitation generated by assuming such a loss to be true, if he never shifts out of the assumption of the reality of the Bright World. If he always assumes that he and his loved ones are eternal beings, even if he temporarily is not experiencing it, he will never have the agitation generated by assuming there is nothing after death.

Explorer begins to see a vast new perspective: The freedom from agitation resulting from holding the assumption that the Bright World and everyone's eternal spirits were real. He views from above, as if in a helicopter, the many times in the past that he had thought he had been forced by traumatic events to shift his assumption.

Explorer could see now that he always had choice. In the future, he can choose the calming assumption rather than the agitating one, in even the most traumatic circumstances.

He isn't sure that he'll always choose wisely to make the calming assumption. The temptation to spice up his life with a little agitation from time to time is there. Explorer could see that he might have to forgive himself again and again for foolishly choosing the path of agitation, but he knows it will be all right in the end.

Then he asks himself: "What would happen if I consistently chose the calming path, assuming the eternal to be more real than earth-plane temporal circumstances?"

He feels himself expanding and growing bigger, filling the enormous space which that possibility opens for him. He travels in that realm until he sees its central essence. As he gradually moves toward it, he feels his heart quicken again with that longing he had felt earlier. He reaches out with his heart and experiences a glorious kaleidoscope of scenes and experiences. They go by too rapidly for him to describe, even to himself. He knows that he sees his loved one's face smiling at him and welcoming him in several of the scenes. When the speed of the shifting scenes becomes too intense for comfort, he finds that he can back away and rest a while. But then the old longing again rises up in his heart, and he moves on. Closer and closer he moves toward the central essence. He remembers the three steps of the Kything formula[3]:

1. I am present to myself.
2. I am present to you. (the central essence in this case).
3. I connect with you.

Explorer continues in his Question-Answer Process:

How can I connect with the central essence?

He can see himself doing a little bow, acknowledging that both he and the essence are present. The bow turns into a little dance that the two of them do with each other, still not touching. They are acknowledging each other's presence, but not connecting yet.

"How can I make the connection?" Explorer asks himself again. The essence seems to speak, Explorer hearing the words in his mind, without them being from an actual voice: "Ask me. Ask me to connect," the essence says. Explorer opens himself, feeling vulnerable but willing to risk it.

"Will you please connect with me?" Explorer asks.

"Of course," comes the answer; "Always. Whenever you ask."

Explorer asks, "Are you real and eternal? Are you really the thing that is totally reliable."

The answer comes: "I am not a thing. I am. You can count on it that I exist and that I enliven all things, but I myself am not a thing."

"How can we connect then?" asks Explorer.

"Dance with me," the answer comes. "And love me with all your heart and soul. We will connect in our movements in the dance. We will meet in our intention to meet. I always intend to connect with you. It is my nature. You have free choice about when to intend to connect with me."

"Why have I not intended to connect with you before?" asks Explorer.

The answer comes: "Remember that you were afraid others important to you would think you were crazy if you assumed it to be true that I existed. They would have rejected you and thrown you out of the tribe. Was your survival dependent on staying in the tribe?"

Explorer thinks back in time. "When I was a child, I was dependent on the family tribe for my physical survival. Now that I am an adult and more independent, it is less true, but still driving me as an assumption that I need to be in the tribe to survive."

"Let me create your new tribe for you," comes the offer. "Let me be the source of creating your family, and I will show you love beyond your wildest dreams. Let go of your idea that families and tribes are created by physical heredity or living together. Take my hand and I will guide you in a dance; we will co-create love incarnate. It will grow from this connection between us as a pine tree grows from a seed, after the searing heat of the forest fire has released it from the cone. Let yourself experience the fire of our connection. Each day spend time and energy focusing your intention on being present with me and making connection in our dance. Let your longing for me burn in you, incomplete, with a gap between us, that is repeatedly bridged by your love flashing across the gap.

"What will I become," asks Explorer, "if I dedicate myself to assuming you and our dance is more real than earth-plane reality?" In his mind, Explorer notices that he is afraid that he will become an alien freak and have no sense of human community.

"What are you already?" comes the answer. "Either you are or you are not an eternal being. What room is there in your human community for an eternal being? Would not an eternal being feel alien there already?"

"Yes," acknowledges Explorer. "There is no room, except possibly the time I spend with my coach, Space-Holder. Here I can experience myself being really me, whatever way that is at the moment, instead of hiding behind what I think others want me to be. Why don't more people want to interact in this way?"

"They have their own paths," comes the answer. "This is yours. No path is better than any other in general, but yours is much the best for you at this time. Embrace it wholeheartedly. Risk the shocks and the longing. They are only the agitated energy of the dross burning off. They are your old inaccurate assumptions. Love brings up whatever is in its way, and those old beliefs are what float and bubble to the surface. Rejoice in experiencing them and letting them go."

"What will I become?" repeats Explorer, fearing the unknown on the other side of such an intense experience.

"You will become a radiant being of love," comes the answer. "This is the being you were meant to be all along. As you radiate your quality of being, love goes out from you and is reflected from whomever has your attention at the moment. The love that is thus reflected back to you, is what you call an experience of love for that person."

"Won't that get me into trouble?" asks Explorer, "indiscriminately loving whomever I happen to be with at the moment?"

"Not if you do not act inappropriately. You always have choice about how to behave," comes the answer.

"But won't I feel this longing for each and everyone I focus on?" asks Explorer. "Won't I be in a constant state of wanting and not having what I want?"

"What, in fact, do you want?" comes the answer.

"I want connection, communion," says Explorer.

"But ask yourself, is not the connection you want, a connection with the loveliness, rather than the person or thing that is lovely?" asks the essence. "Is not what you want to connect with, the eternal which you see reflected back to you from the face you are looking at, not the face itself? Your connection with the eternal within you, which is the source of your radiance, is where your longing can be satisfied. Come to me within yourself. Find me and love me. Know that our love is the most real experience in your life."

"How do I manage to perform as a human?" asks Explorer. "This love will flow from our dance through me and out into the world. I will see you reflected in the images of the world, and I will get confused and think you are out there. There is danger that I will become hooked into the material world."

"Remember," comes the answer, "that you are a third thing, whose existence is even more real than either of the other two things: You are senior to the things you have designated as good in the physical world, and you are also senior to all this spiritual fire. You are the one above them both, the one who is the chooser. Sometimes you choose to experience the good in the world and sometimes you choose to experience the transilient good within yourself. Play with your choices lightly. You are not locked into either."

"Who am I then?" an awe-struck Explorer asks.

"You are just you," comes the answer. "In just being you, you are more divine and closer to source than any-thing or anyone else in your experience, including me. Honor yourself as being that special."

Explorer starts to ask himself how he can be certain this is true, but quickly reminds himself that this is another case of needing to assume it, in order to have certainty about it being true. He laughs and feels light hearted again. He gives Space-Holder a big hug, thanking him for enabling Explorer to get in touch with himself again. Space-Holder picks up his flute and starts playing a spirited tune, his eyes sparkling. Explorer moves off singing a happy tune, and experimenting with new steps in his dance of life.

Chapter 13

Blocked Feelings Regarding One's Own Death

Explorer's glow and joy, which he had found in opening up his heart, enables him to live with a radiant feeling of aliveness for a long time. But one day, he feels that he is colliding with a harsh wall. He does not feel able to handle it by himself, so he starts looking for Space-Holder.

"Where can he be," he wonders. "He's almost always easy to spot."

The country along the bank is fairly open, populated with oaks and a few firs. Explorer finally spies Space-Holder stretched out on a broad tree limb, relaxing and gazing raptly at the grass and wild flowers beneath him. He greets him fondly and they settle down under the tree to talk about Explorer's problem.

"I think I know what this harsh wall is," says Explorer. "In our last talk, I managed to transcend the death of my loved one, but now I am confronting my own death and this seems like a different sort of problem.

"Yes, quite so," agrees Space-Holder. "Is there any particular reason for your thinking of your own death right now?"

"Well, I'm no longer young, but I hope and expect to have many more enjoyable years before I die of old age. However, several friends of mine have recently died and it has come into my mind that it is always possible that I will get some dread disease and die much sooner than I have planned. This idea has made me realize that I need to work on my own dying. Whenever it happens, I want to have done my homework, and know how to handle it. When I try to confront my own death consciously, I find that I hit this harsh wall and bounce off before I can handle it.

"Do you have a first question?" asks Space-Holder.

"My mind just seems to curl up all bruised and scraped by the wall. I can't seem to focus on anything," replies Explorer.

"Let's think of something to give it relief so it can function thoughtfully again," says Space-Holder.

"How can we do that?" asks Explorer.

"Ask yourself," suggests Space-Holder. "That sounds like a good first question."

Explorer agrees and settles down to put the question in his own terms:

What assumption, if I made it, would give my mind comfort and relief?

If I could assume that who I am is a being who is able to rise above this death problem and see it from the vantage point of a bird flying over it— rather than being involved in it, to observe it. In order to create that perspective, I notice that I have to assume that my mind will not be significantly affected by either the dying process or being dead. That doesn't sound like a realistic assumption to me. In the cases of friends whom I have observed going through the dying process, their minds went through all kinds of emotional upsets before they came to a state of acceptance about the fact of their dying. Then, they went through various lengths of time being sedated or comatose, finally ending in being dead.

From my observer's point of view, it seemed to me that their minds were very significantly affected by the whole process. I guess that I could assume that once they were safely dead, their minds could come awake, focused and calm again after their processing or whatever the other side uses for that kind of healing. It is a little hard to trust that this is what happens when it's my own mind that is being put through it all. It's hard to trust that the guardian angels or spiritual beings or whoever will be in charge of that for me will be Johnny-on-the-spot to take charge of resuscitating my consciousness. I have been used to having my consciousness at my own disposal. Dying seems different from just having surgical anesthesia where one is not aware of time passing until one wakes up in pain in the recovery room. After surgery I know that I will be in charge again, consciously speaking. On the other hand, with this dying process, I am having trouble trusting that I won't just get left in a disjointed spiritual backwater, unconscious with no one paying any attention to my needs."

"There certainly is the necessity for trusting in a situation like that," concurs Space-Holder. "Would you like to try asking yourself when it was that you decided that there was a chance you might be left in a spiritual backwater, unconscious, untended and unloved?"

Explorer tries to think back to when he had made that assumption. It seems to be at various times in this and other previous lifetimes. "I was usually observing the death of others while I was still in the belief that there was nothing after death. I saw that their consciousness was gone from here—so completely gone I could not sense them psychically any more the way I had been used to sensing them. It seemed as if they just suddenly were non-existent. If there is life after death, it must be a different sort of thing from this life or my psychic connection with them would not be severed so completely."

"You experienced dialoguing with your loved one in our last talk. How was it different from your psychic experience of connecting with him when he was alive?" Space-Holder asks.

"It was just as if it were in my imagination—it did not seem very real. It was not at all like the experience of being with a physical person who is independent and acts out of his own free will. This dialogue in my imagination could be all made up by me," observes Explorer, who continues in the Question-Answer Process:

> *How do I know the spirit of my loved one was a real and independent psychic being, and not just my imagination?*
>
> How do I know anything? I assume it is true and see if that assumption works best.
>
> *Did it work best last time?*
>
> Yes, definitely.

"Therefore, I will assume that it is true," continues Explorer, "but there is still this discontinuity problem."

Space-Holder interjects the idea that there might be something to be learned from the discontinuity everyone experiences on waking up from sleep. "Notice," he says, "that there is no discontinuity on falling into sleep. Have you ever been aware of the first moment of being asleep?"

"No," admits Explorer. "I just seem to go on doing whatever I am psychically doing until suddenly I realize there is a discontinuity and I am awake again. In retrospect I assume that I must have fallen asleep earlier and dreamed in the mean time."

"What does that discontinuity of coming awake have to say about your assumptions regarding dying?" asks Space-Holder.

"What comes up for me," says Explorer, "is that I do not want to go to sleep by dying while knowing that I will not have the experience of the discontinuity of waking up again."

"Is there something special about that discontinuity of waking up?" asks Space-Holder.

"Yes," says Explorer. "It is my most consistently spiritually energizing time. In that time just after wakening, while still relaxed, warm, and half asleep, I experience what I call the golden energy—the Holy Spirit or divine energy moving through me. Those times are very precious for me." Explorer continues in the Question-Answer Process:

Do I believe that if I am dead, I will not have those wonderful experiences on waking up?

Yes, I guess that is what I do believe. Odd but true. That discontinuity experience on waking from sleep is what I believe I will not have when I am dead.

Will I have those experiences when am dead?

No. Being dead is psychically different from being alive.

Is there some other way that I can be nurtured by the golden energy when I am dead?

No. It seems to me that this golden energy experience is only available to those who are psychically incarnate in a body on earth-plane.

Is that because I will not need such experiences when I am safely dead?

Yes. I get the image of scuba divers who relish each breath of oxygen from their hoses connected to oxygen tanks, but once they are back on the surface they no longer need such a vehicle to give them life-sustaining air.

Why can't I trust that idea as applied to my dying?

I think I will still be underwater in the scuba analogy and that I will need it. I guess I can't imagine not needing it.

Space-Holder interjects: "You found the spirit of your loved one, last time, through your heart connection—through what your heart was longing for. Is there something about the heart of the universe longing for you that would be useful to assume here?" he asks.

"Yes," says Explorer. "That brings tears to my eyes, the idea that somebody would reach out to me with love that would be strong, warm, and exist whether I was alive or safely dead. I guess I thought probably rightly that no human love, love from humans still alive and in their bodies, could reach across the grave. I haven't thought there was love from the heart of the universe that I could ride on or beam in on in the dying process and afterward. I guess it would be sensible to beam in on it, even before the dying process—to get the relationship established so it is there when I need it.

"If I could assume there was this massive love from the heart of the universe for me, I can feel that it would dissolve the problem of the harsh wall I experienced when thinking of my own dying." Explorer continues in the Question-Answer Process:

Why am I reluctant to assume it?

The family and friends I grew up with would put me down and make fun of it if I let them know that I believed such a thing. I can feel their absolute prohibition of believing such a thing.

Why were they like that?

Who knows? They just were—probably none of my business. My business is to decide what I am going to assume to be true now.

Am I afraid of what damage their derision would do to me? Or what my outrageous assumption would do to them? Or the damage derision or outrageousness would do to our relationship?

The damage to our relationship. It was all I had, I thought, while growing up. I was very dependent on it then probably for my very survival. But now that I am an independent adult, I can risk the loss of the relationship especially when the potential rewards seem so great.

Am I now willing to assume that the heart of the universe reaches out to me in love, and will continue to do so through the dying, death, and after death process?

Yes, but I will need to practice with it for a while before I can be steady and good at assuming it. It still is a little new and amazing.

Could the universe really be so wonderful?

Space-Holder chuckles and interjects: "Why not?" They sit together quietly and watch the sunset for awhile, Explorer gingerly experimenting with his new-found assumption.

Chapter 14

Life Doesn't Seem to be Working

This day Explorer finds himself unhappy. He's been so buffeted by the small disappointments and frustrations in his everyday life, that no longer can he create steady feelings of good energy. He feels confused and fragmented, despairing that he can ever learn to do it right. He paddles over to the bank and spies Space-Holder resting peacefully on a grassy slope in the shade of a tree. "I wonder how he always happens to be where I pull up to the bank," muses Explorer. He drops down on the grass, sighs, and waits for Space-Holder to open an eye. As soon as he does, Explorer mournfully asks him if he really thinks he could help out with yet another problem.

Space-Holder looks up and smiles at his old friend. Before he can utter a greeting, the words tumble out of Explorer's mouth, a litany of his most recent unhappy experiences. Space-Holder listens awhile, then holds up his hand to stop the outpouring and replies calmly in response to Explorer's despair.

"An especially important thing to remember," he begins, "is that there are two different parts of us that are wounded by any upsetting event. It is crucial to differentiate between them because they are healed by opposite processes."

Upon hearing these few words, Explorer is amazed to note that a glimmer of hope already is seeping in to his feelings. Space-Holder proceeds. "One thing that gets wounded is our *truth*, our personal structure of reality that assumed this kind of event would not happen. The other wounded part is our *good*, both our good feelings and our own good story. The repeated events have again and again smashed our hope and shattered our good story. Life's just that way. We think up something good that we believe will happen, and somehow it rarely turns out that way. Most of us have fallen into the trap of equating the attainment of our expected outcomes with Life telling us we're doing it right. The fact is there is no such equation and we don't get all our expected outcomes. So gradually, over time, if we depend on good outcomes this way, we can't help but conclude that we aren't doing it right, never can and never will.

"This is a very despairing conclusion. It comes from trying to use the same process to heal our wounded *good story* as to heal our wounded *truth*. That just doesn't work. Let me explain.

"The way we know we are doing it right when healing our truth, that is, our sense of what is real and so, is to experience a calmness that follows a transfixing process. This is a process wherein we assume to be true that which is real. In order to ascertain what is real, we do some detective work about what's happened, make our best guess about the facts, and then firmly structure our reality by assuming those facts are true. We see that the upset happened in such and such a way, and ended up with certain results. We face the results and assume that they're real and true. We can tell if we're doing it right if we feel calm and stable in this revised view of reality.

"Let me give you an example. Let's say I heard that a person I previously trusted had made a negative judge-ment about me and called me a bad name in public. I'm not only shocked and dismayed when I hear this, but I can't believe this person would do such a thing. So my first step in healing my sense of what's true is to determine what's real. I start my detective work to ascertain the facts as well as I can. I find out that the person really did say it and that this really did upset me. I admit to myself that the person really can behave that way and say such upsetting things. When I do this, I suddenly feel calmer because I've replaced my previous inaccurate view with a more accurate view of reality."

"Is it really that simple to recover your calm feeling?" asks Explorer. "Don't you have to work through your upset feelings like the sensitivity groups do?"

"Yes it is," says Space-Holder, "works every time to heal the upset of the unreality and you don't have to spend a lot of time and energy working through upset feelings. They just disappear once you get to the truth.

"Next we'll work on the lack of energy and enthusiasm that has resulted from the wounded good story. The healing process for our *good story* is a transilient one, even though it's true that something transfixed, our good story, has been wounded. The process for healing our good story is *not* to firmly assume new transfixed assumptions about what's good. If you've ever tried to do that, you know it doesn't work. When you wanted your good story to happen one particular way—such as, your unique child should be well and grow up healthy and happy—the pain following this particular child's death can't be healed simply by assuming the good story that another child is alive and well. You wanted the dead child to survive, and you feel cruel pain that it didn't turn out that way.

"The process for healing our *good* is not to immediately superimpose a *new good* over the shattered *old good*. You can't judge if you are doing the healing process right by looking at whether you have a new stable good story in place. That just doesn't work. What works is first to create the transilient good feelings in the now, and slowly over time, watch as a new good story grows in your life.

"Let's exemplify this. In the case of my hearing I was called a bad name, I was able to reach a calm feeling by seeing the new truth about what really happened, but I wasn't yet able to have good feelings and enthusiasm. The first step is to abandon the transfixed idea that I can, in the future, trust the person not to be that way. I give up focusing on the future and stay in the present. I pay attention to the good that's around me and tune in on my inner being and the universal spirit in me. I stay in the now leading my everyday life. Eventually, I notice a new vision of a trusting future arising; within it is room for people that can be trusted and a distancing from those that can't.

Explorer then asks the obvious question: "So how can I know if I'm doing it right in the meantime? I can't look to see if I have a stable new good story because it won't be created yet. So many of our good stories end up as shambled wrecks. So few turn out exactly the way we plan them. No wonder I'm in despair if I have no way of knowing whether I am doing the healing process right!"

Space-Holder suggests that Explorer do his own question-answer process about this problem.

Explorer begins with the question:

How can I determine whether I am doing the healing-of-the-good process right?

I could just assume that whatever I am doing is right, but that lacks discrimination. Some things I could do must be more useful than other things. I need some kind of feedback to judge this rightly.

What feedback could I use to judge this?

It might have to do with whether I am having feelings of good energy right now. However, I would need to allow myself to have grieving feelings, without invalidating the whole process.

What percent of the time would I have to have good feelings in order to judge that I was doing it right?

Enough of the time to keep my spirit alive and not in general despair.

How much is that?

Whatever it takes. I could judge it by whether my spirit is alive and able to make positive assumptions rather than bogged down in despairing ones such as "nothing good ever turns out right."

If I find I am not doing it right, like now, how do I get myself to doing it right?

I can see that it would help not to over-generalize— I can say that it is true that these particular things didn't turn out the way I wanted them to, but that doesn't necessarily mean that nothing will ever turn out the way I want. However, just eliminating over-generalizing doesn't seem to generate much good transilient energy.

What could I do, in addition to eliminating over-generalizing, to open myself to more transilient good feelings?

The basic transilient assumption that "Everything is perfect; nothing in the world is better than anything else" would be useful but I usually can't make it when I feel trapped in a painful shattered good story.

So in those circumstances, what assumptions would be a first step?

To confront whatever feeling I am having and experience it. Then assume that if I feel it enough, and look for the assumption that is generating the pain, I can find a new calming assumption. (Pauses) Hmmm—eventually I will arrive at a calmness where I will have choice. There I can make some transilience-opening assumptions such as "God loves me. I am doing it right." Then I can be enough in touch with the force for good in the universe for it to infuse me with good feelings, warmth, love and joy. But when I reach that choice level, and start having good feelings and energy, I often think I shouldn't wallow in it—that it would be indulging myself and might not be doing it right.

When did I decide that having good feeling energy meant I was doing it wrong?

Every time something turned out wrong, I looked back to see what to blame for it; often I'd been feeling good energy before it happened and so I blamed the good energy feelings for having it turn out wrong.

When was the first time I did that and what had just happened?

I get images as a kid of feeling really good and cutting up around the house and having suddenly been slapped— which I concluded happened because I was feeling good.

Can I talk to the kid I was, who was getting slapped, and negotiate a different conclusion?

The kid I was says that having good feelings made me be relaxed and not watchful enough of my parents' bad feelings so I didn't guard myself enough from their reaction. Oh, I also just realized that Jesus got slapped in the form of crucifixion and then rose above it by not taking it personally.

Is that what I am supposed to do with all slaps? Not take them personally?

What else is there to do with slaps? Distance from being slapped, if I can.

Won't I be in danger of submitting to an abusive situation if I don't take the slaps personally?

You don't have to take the slaps personally, or blame your good feelings for causing the slaps, in order to do whatever you can to distance from the slapper.

"But I'm still left with this kid part of me making the conclusion that feeling good was the cause of getting slapped," complained Explorer.

Space-Holder breaks in to comment that it was true that a person who was feeling bad, grumpy and angry might react by slapping someone who was demonstrating good feelings. "This angry person often believes everyone should feel as bad," he said, "until something makes him feel better. And since he has free will not to change the assumptions that are at the root of the anger and grumpiness, there's no way to force the healing of such an angry person. His anger and slapping will make someone else angry, and on and on until it seems there is no end to the contagious epidemic of angry bad feelings. There has to be a different way to handle it or all is lost.

"The way I am suggesting you might handle it," declares Space-Holder, "is never to blame the good feelings; only blame the slapper for doing it wrong. Never join the slapper in trying to suppress the good feelings. When the sting of the slap has faded, you again have a choice. Choose to create more good feelings, and assume they will eventually grow a new good story in which the slappers of the world won't prevail."

Explorer pauses a moment to contemplate that, then continues his process:

How do I create good feelings when the sting of the slap has faded?

Assume some transilient good assumptions and let the good feelings nurture me, instead of shying away from the feelings as being the cause of the shattering events.

What should I do with the slapper?

Experiment with a new way to protect myself from the slapper without losing intention and capacity to create joy in my own inner feelings.

What transilient good assumption can I make right now?

'God loves me, and I am doing it right.'

If I make this assumption, do I feel good transilient energy now?

Explorer squeezes his closed eyes and tries the assumptions on for size by assuming they are true: 'God loves me, and I am doing it right'.

Yes! Amazingly, I feel better already.

How can I do it so that I will not lose this good feeling in the future?

Well, it looks like I will lose it temporarily every time another good story gets shattered. I can feel bad by just misplacing my car keys. But now I know how to get the good feelings back again. I know I can make some transilient good assumptions. I also know that it is my responsibility to do it. No one else can make assumptions for me, although they can remind me of some possibilities.

This responsibility to make my own assumptions that work best must be what people are talking about when they claim that we each create our own reality. It is not so much that we create the events that shatter our good stories. It is that we create the feelings we have in the face of such events. Yes, it is the reality of our inner experience that we create. We have the opportunity to calm agitation by correcting our transfixed assumptions to those that are true, and to generate good energy feelings by coming back into the present moment and making some transilient good assumptions.

How do I eventually have any new good stories? Do I ask myself what is wrong in the world, with the intention to fix it?

No. That just gets me into agitation. Thinking that something is wrong in the world conflicts with the truth that I am assuming (in the transilient good moment) that everything is all right.

So how do I generate a new good story?

As Joseph Campbell said, I follow my bliss. I notice what I love, and weave a good story from that.

What generates my feeling that I love something or someone?

The good feelings from making transilient good assumptions get more and more intense, warming my inner experience and my heart. I become a radiant with love. As I radiate this energy into the world, it is reflected back to me by who and what is under my nose—who and what my attention is focused on—and I experience them as being lovable, and then I love them.

Isn't that non-discriminating? Wouldn't I just love anything or anyone that I put my attention on?

Yes. That is how God loves, isn't it? And I always have a choice about what to put my attention on.

Could I become one of those robust full-of-life persons who radiate joy and seem to love the whole world? Could I do that by just starting with factual truth, and some transilient good assumptions, such as 'God loves me, and I am doing it right'?

I will have to try it and see if it works.

Explorer opens his eyes, smiling. He stands up, stretches and thanks Space-Holder who nods his approval. Explorer says he's eager to try what he saw in the processing and goes bounding off to experiment with his newly understood principles.

Chapter 15

A Problem with God

Explorer has been doing quite well with his navigating on the river and with his relationships. However, he has been running into difficulties with the higher order aspects of his existence. He hankers for a talk with Space-Holder, starts looking for his old friend and finds him again under the same tree. The time of their meetings is falling into a regular rhythm—a kind of rap session where occasionally they switch roles, Explorer providing the atmosphere for Space-Holder to do some question-answer process too. This time Explorer is wrestling with his "spiritual trip."

"I have a problem with God," begins Explorer. "I have gotten over being angry at God for all the bad things that have happened in the world, and I understand that a most important part of my spiritual life is my relationship with him, but I can't seem to relate to an entity so diffuse and nebulous. My idea of relationship seems to include, of necessity, a very focused attention on someone or something unique and specific. Maybe this comes from my culture's view that a loving relationship between equals is usually romantic. A loving relationship between non-equals, like the old paternalistic view of God as the father, isn't what I want. I want my relationship with God to be as equal co-creators. Maybe we have a difference in function, but I want us to be equal in value and importance. My role would be to make assumptions and God's to pour forth energy."

Space-Holder joins in, saying, "There are several references in the Bible to a relationship with God being like a romantic one: There is Jesus' story of the wise virgins getting to marry the Bridegroom because they kept their lamps filled with oil and ready to light. That was in contrast to the foolish virgins who let their lamps run dry. There is also, of course the beautiful love poem, *The Song of Solomon*, though scholars can't seem to decide if this poem describes the love between us and God or if it was just a human love poem that was too beautiful not to include in the Bible. It is my impression that while all configurations of our relationship with God should be explored, that the most meaningful and energizing one is often found between a person and the manifestation of God as the opposite sex—that is, a woman would find it in a relationship to a male image of God and a man to a female image of God."[4]

Explorer nods his understanding and continues to relate his problem: "Jews and Christians alike advocate that we love the Lord our God with all our strength and all our heart and all our mind, but they don't seem to discuss how to love something so universal. If God is everywhere, I can't seem to clearly relate to him. I can love God for creating all the beautiful things in the world—a sort of warm fuzzy affection—but I can't seem to get a really enlivening process going with such a diffuse God."

Explorer continues: "There is the old paradoxical saying about God that, 'This also is Thou—Neither is this Thou.' God is everything and/or nothing. That doesn't help me either in connecting with God in a relationship.

"Then there are all those people who claim they can hear or sense God talking to them and they tell about it or print leaflets. But I know when answers come up for me in my question-answer process, I can't tell where they are coming from—and sometimes those answers are right on and sometimes they are off the wall so how could I trust myself to know if I was really talking to God or not? I've read enough about spirit beings on the astral planes to know that there can be bad spirits pretending to be God, so how would I know? My psychic receiving device, such as it is, doesn't seem able to screen out such impostors. I think I just pick up whoever is broadcasting. I can ask my questions while concentrating on speaking with God, but heaven knows whose answers I'd be picking up. That just doesn't seem like a trustable method for the intense and vulnerable personal relationship I am envisioning with God."

Space holder thinks a minute, then comments, "Perhaps that is what people use altars for—to have stable visual symbols of God they can relate to."

Explorer complains, "How can I use somebody's prettied up version of what they think God looks like as the focus for the most important relationship in my life? All those altar images look different from each other. Which one is right? How could any static picture be representative enough of God for me to form a real relationship? God has to be able to respond and let me know his position on things, for it to be real and reciprocal."

Space-Holder then suggests Explorer try doing the question-answer process on the problem.

Explorer slouches lower on the grass feeling grumpy and resistant, but begins:

What words would express my grumpiness?

'I'm not going to get suckered in again.'

When did I get suckered in before?

Recently, every time I created a new good story it seemed I was co-creating it with the enlivening energy of God. Every time the good story got shattered, I got mad at God.

Am I trying to prevent myself from getting mad at God? Am I insisting on an experience that will be guaranteed to grow a new good story that won't get shattered?

I guess I am. I guess I'm looking for a relationship with God in which I'd both love him with all my strength, heart and mind, and in which I would never have to go through any disappointing shattering loss. It would be me giving out love and God always being there to love and to love me back. — always energizing and nurturing; never a downer.

Is that a realistic expectation?"

It would mean that I would be forever above and beyond disappointment. That looks pretty good to me in my present state but maybe it would be overdoing it—like someone dying of thirst in the desert praying for water and getting drowned in a flash flood.

Is my desired picture of my relationship with God overdoing a desire for a stable wonderfulness?

Probably, but I don't want to make any more good stories that are going to crash and burn. I can't stand that any more. What is my next question?

Am I in such a traumatized state that I have to do some healing before I can create any new good stories?

Yes, it seems like that.

So how do I heal this state without any new good story?

Go with transilient good and rest there as long as it takes.

What assumption would enable me to get from here into the transilient good state?

God loves me.

Can I assume that?

I can assume 'God loves me' without sensing him as a discrete being, because I can judge whether I'm doing it right by whether the energy coming in is nurturing and loving or not.

But aren't I supposed to love God in return in this relationship?

Yes, eventually, after I am more healed.

How is my being more healed going to relieve my need for God to be a more specific being to make it easier for me to direct my love?

Maybe that isn't the way it works between us and God.

Then why do the scriptures tell us to love the Lord our God with all our strength and heart and mind if what we are supposed to do is assume that God loves us, instead of us loving God.

Those old bozos who wrote the Bible couldn't believe themselves worthy of God loving them unless they did something worthy first, such as loving God.

What about Dante being sparked by Beatrice? He only got one smile from her, and he used it to build his poetic way to Paradise.

Notice that it began with her smiling at him—her loving him. The initiating fact for Dante was that he was loved. It was only secondary that he loved her, though that's what he concentrated his poetry on.

Is it important to ask for the love, or be open to it, or desire it?

Desiring the love is in itself a good story. The story is that I don't have the love now and I long for it, desire it, and ask for it. Dante asked for it merely by looking Beatrice's way on the street that one morning. It didn't matter to him that others might love him—his mother, his friends, his dog. He was asking for a particular type of love and Beatrice smiling at him gave it to him. That was the initiating catalyst for all the energy of his love for her that poured forth in his poetry and enabled him to experience Paradise.

How did Beatrice's one loving smile trigger all that energy in him?

The same way that my assuming God loves me will trigger healing energy in me. First, I need to have clearly asked for what I desire, the stable continuing, reliable experience of being loved. (This is an example of why we need to be specific in praying for something.) Second, I need to assume that God loves me.

What if God doesn't love me at some point in time—if he is in a bad mood or is distracted by other events?

Then I won't experience being loved by God for that time, but it seems like God has a pretty steady supply of love for all of us most all the time.

Does God's love vary in intensity from time to time?

How does my love for my family members vary in intensity? That might be a good model. I always love them but sometimes I experience it more than others, and sometimes I experience a different and stronger emotion toward them such as anger on top of the love. But my love is always there for my family members. That may be similar to God's love being always there for each of us.

Does God ever get angry on top of his love?

The Old Testament seemed to say so but Jesus had a different idea that emphasized the love more.

So, is my love for God not the initial generating factor here?

True. What I want to generate is an experience of the energy—good transilient energy—of God's love for me. It is not generated by my loving God—so I don't have to focus on God as unique and specifically lovable. God's loving me is a constant—a given—a fact of my existence. My experience of it is triggered by opening to it—by assuming it is true: 'God loves me.'

Will I love God because I experience God's love for me?

You will love whatever is under your nose—whatever you see. If you have God under your nose, it will remind you to continue assuming God is loving you.

Do I have any other resistance to assuming God is loving me?

It feels a little childish—like a child being loved by a parent—rather than the love of co-creating equals that I was looking for.

Is God's love for me like a father loving a child?

Ask for it the way you want it.

Should I change the assumption to "God loves me as a co-creating equal?"

Try it and see if it works as well.

Explorer closes his eyes and tries the new assumption.

"That seems scary," Explorer continues, "it gives me more responsibility—but that is what I wanted so I'll stay with it awhile and see how it works.

"This new view of thinking—that the generating act is my making the assumption that 'God loves me'— enables the stability of this experience to be in *my* hands, under *my* control. The only way this good story could get shattered is by my changing to a different assumption. Since I am always in charge of what I am assuming to be true, it puts me in charge of whether I have this experience of loving energy or not. This may be the good story I was looking for that won't get shattered."

Space-Holder interrupted at this point. He said, "You have just touched on something extremely important that appears to run counter to how most people have thought the universe runs. They believe that the universal relationships are fixed and they must find the right rules to follow in order to be safe. They haven't recognized their partnership in the whole process. If they heard what you just said, they would reject that it all could come from something as simple as personal assumptions. To them, this would seem self-centered, arbitrary and dangerous—allowing anyone to create any crazy assumption at any time. They believe that there's some truth and a set of rules outside of them that they have to find and follow in detail in order to be safe. The point is, that God and we have been created as partners. Our ability to invoke assumptions lets us experience the truth of our relationship. The mechanism is simple and powerful, if I feel calmed, the assumption is true and is in alignment with ultimate reality. If my experience is agitation or upset, the mechanism is telling me the assumption is off the mark."

Explorer thinks it over for a minute then says, "It all seems to fit for me now—my stabilizing the experience of loving energy through assuming that 'God loves me.' I suppose I might get bored or overly confident sometime and want the scary thrill of trying to live life without this loving energy, but it will be a long time in the future before I try it."

Space-Holder points out, "There are still a lot of people out there who don't assume God loves them. Don't you want to go out and save them by figuring out a way to get them to assume 'God loves me'?"

Explorer laughs and says, "I see that I have been doing that recently, trying to save the world. I don't think I have to do that again for a long time."

Explorer tells Space-Holder that he feels a lot clearer about his relationship to the higher order aspects of existence and thanks him for his help. Explorer then ambles off, dedicating himself to his own continued healing before he tries to take on the world again.

Chapter 16

Not Feeling Truly Known

Explorer is feeling lonely. He feels reluctant to go to Space-Holder with this problem because he is afraid it would look as though he is using Space-Holder's company to fill his, Explorer's, loneliness. But today, the need to feel he is known by someone for who he really is becomes so acute that he is willing to risk being misunderstood. He needs his old friend and coach, Space-Holder, to be with him while he works on the problem.

He finds Space-Holder under his usual tree, and sits down beside him. Explorer asks if Space-Holder thinks this is an appropriate problem to work on. Space-Holder smiles a little and says, gently, that of course it is a worthy and even crucial problem.

Explorer sighs and settles down to begin working. Space-Holder suggests that Explorer start by focusing on how he experiences the problem in his bodily sensations and feelings.

Explorer closes his eyes to concentrate more intently on what he is feeling in his body. What he notices first is a gnawing, agitated longing in his heart. He decides to use the question-answer process:

> *If this feeling expressed itself in words, what would they be?*
>
> I want someone to know me.
>
> *When did I decide I wasn't known?*

Always. This is an on-going present time problem.

What assumption do I have that is generating this upsetting feeling of not being known?

That it is essential to be known or I'll be lost forever.

What new assumption could I make that would calm this agitation?

That I really am known because God knows me. His knowing me is an important part of the assumption about God loving me. If he didn't know me, his love would be meaningless.

"That calms and warms me," muses Explorer, "but it still feels as though I want some incarnate human person to know me and feel positive about me whether or not that positive feeling could be called love." He continues the process:

Why do I particularly want a human person to know me? Why is God not enough?

If I am not known by another human person, I feel out of touch with the whole human network. It feels as if there is no place to interface and join in with the human race. I feel disconnected from everyone and that I can't find a place to hold on—a sort of hand-hold—holding someone else's hand so as to interact with him either by me helping him or his helping me. Even just a squeeze of hands to acknowledge each other's presence. I want a greeting by at least one person who knows me and understands me and knows where I am coming from and shares my values enough to be able to appreciate me.

Does that mean the other person would have to share my or a similar good story?

134

No, it is more like sharing the same values, outlook and attitudes. Not so much in the sense of a shared past good story, though I suppose some people try to base their feeling of being known on a shared past, it is more like sharing present time values, but even that isn't quite it. What I want is not to be the same as the person who knows me. I want to be unique and known by another unique being. Perhaps this is why God's knowing me isn't enough. God is everything which is too diffuse to be unique and separate from me.

Space-Holder rummages around in his backpack and pulls out an article by Maurice Friedman, the biographer of Martin Buber, in which Space-Holder describes Friedman's writing that the I-Thou dialogue is essential to the experience of our own uniqueness. He reads from the article: (Page 20) "It is only holding our ground in openness and trust that we can experience and know him (the other person) as a person in a relationship in which his uniqueness becomes manifest in coming up against our uniqueness. Otherwise, what we see is a distortion of him—the way he is when he has not a real person to come up against."

Space-Holder turns back some pages and continues reading (Page 12): "Dialogue means a mutual sharing in reciprocal presentness of the unique. The unique implies otherness but otherness capable of entering into communion."[5]

Space-Holder adds, "In his book, *A Different Drum,* Scott Peck calls this 'communion' the entering into the spirit of community."

"In the past," comments Explorer, "I have called this 'minds meeting in the light with goodwill'." Explorer stares down at the ground momentarily, then continues in his process:

Why does this special type of interaction—where I am known—feel so important to me?

It is because that is the only time I'm able to feel I'm truly being myself. That's when I really live, as opposed to living for others.

Why does my uniqueness need someone else's uniqueness to push against in order to exist?

It isn't that my uniqueness butts up against the other person's uniqueness. In a dialogue first one speaks and then the other responds. They don't speak simultaneously. While one is speaking from his soul, the other is silent and open—yet generating a sort of psychic wind from the bare rocks of his silent soul. This psychic wind acts as a force that blows away the non-essential elements of the current speaker's ideas, enabling him to perceive more clearly the actuality of his experience and to think more clearly when finding old assumptions and making new ones.

I can see that this strips me down to the real me, but why do I value that so much?

When else am I truly alive? When else can I firmly act and take the next step in my spiritual journey?

Given that it is accurate that this experience of being known is so crucial, how do I create more of it in my life?

Actively seek such a dialogue being as real as I can be. Right from my soul, I should test each relationship until the other person I am testing turns to foggy mush or courageously goes on meeting the challenge of the real me. I can't tell if a person wants to meet me in this exchange unless I test him. Keep testing until I find a few who rise to my greeting and then nurture and value them greatly. They will be priceless in my life.

What do I do with my longing for it in the meantime?

I guess it is like any desire: I assume I already have it. This will enable me to turn from desire for the future good to being in the present moment where I can make some transilient good assumptions and nurture myself.

Which transilient good assumptions would help here?

Here are a few: 'In this present moment, I am already all that I am meant to be.' 'In the warm enlivening energy of this moment, I rejoice and give thanks for the universe meeting my needs.' 'Always I will tread these paths with the beautiful energy making my soul glow with the glory of God.' 'In this present moment, there exists unknown to me as yet, many souls who are capable of meeting my soul, my uniqueness known by their uniqueness.'

Explorer asks Space-Holder if he experiences the meetings with him, Explorer, in that way.

Space-Holder smiles and nods, saying, "I am as grateful for the wind off the bare rocks of your soul as you are for mine. These things are mutual or they don't work well at all."

Explorer pushes further and asks Space-Holder if he doesn't have a problem to do the question-answer process about, while Explorer remains open for him.

Space-Holder stretches and rolls over on his stomach, supporting himself with his elbows on the grass, and turning within to see if he has something to work on. What comes up is an image of beautiful castles in the sky changing and moving within each other.

Space-Holder goes into his own question-answer process:

Is this an image of the New Jerusalem as described by John in The Book of Revelations?

This is the same thing John saw but you can see it more accurately now than you would be able to envision it from John's description.

What is the significance of my seeing this now?

I am feeling a little homesick.

What am I feeling I am missing?

Let the image unfold and I will see it.

The image unfolds until Space-Holder envisions a transilient glowing green stone.

What does this green stone mean?

Dialogue with the stone.

Stone says: Call me to you, you who feel heavily ladened.

Space-Holder says: How do I call you?

Stone: Love me.

Space-Holder: I am doing that and I merge with you, become you and now I feel crystalline structure transfixing me and radiant green light pulsating through me.

Stone: Stay with me and I will heal your world weariness.

Space-Holder: Thank you so much. This feels wonderful and I think I'll stay here for awhile.

Explorer looks down on his serene friend. He waits a moment, then starts to depart.

"See you next time, Explorer," grins Space-Holder. "Thanks for being with me today."

Chapter 17

Feeling Betrayed in a Spiritual Support Group

Explorer runs up the bank in a highly agitated state, throwing himself on the ground beside Space-Holder, who sits in his favorite spot under a tree. "What on earth has made you so agitated?" asks Space-Holder who is concerned to see his friend so upset.

"I feel so betrayed," wails Explorer. "I have belonged to a spiritual support group for some time," he said shakily. "It is led by a man who seemed at first to be a worthy person. I counted on this man to be my spiritual guide and he just sacrificed me to his own paranoid ego. I can't believe this could happen," he moaned. "I was very cautious about getting involved in his group at the beginning and checked him out every way I knew how. I admit I was very hungry for a spiritual leader who could create a supportive and enlightening group. I really felt a need to belong to some sort of organized spiritual body with an enlightened atmosphere. I've seen studies that show there is much benefit in healing and nurturing, both physically and spiritually, in participating with a number of others of like mind."

Space-Holder concurs. "Certainly the study of support groups of metastatic breast cancer patients done at Stanford[6] showed that the patients in the groups lived twice as long on the average (36 months) as the patients in the control section without such a group (18 months). The doctors running the study didn't expect such significant results, but spiritual leaders in general weren't surprised. Jesus said that where two or more people meet in his name, he would be there too in spirit—he was referring to the same general principle. Scott Peck wrote about it at length in his book, *A Different Drum.* He said that the difference between effective groups and ineffective or damaging groups was whether the participants achieved a spirit of community. He described the key element of building such a community feeling was that the members empty themselves of opinions and attempts to heal or convert each other. Instead, they were to really listen to each other.

"I once tried a variation of that," continues Space-Holder, "by leading some groups in which they were silent until someone felt moved to speak in the question-answer process. The others were instructed to listen to the person doing the process until he reached some clarity in the matter, and then to give only enough feedback so he knew he had been heard. It worked marvelously well for people being able to reveal themselves on a deep intimate level, but they complained after only a few weeks of meetings that it was all too intense and scary. It demanded more than they wanted to put into such a group. How was your group structured?"

Explorer describes his group as sharing his belief in the efficacy of finding one's inaccurate assumptions and shifting to truer ones. The format of the group had been based on praying together. Each person in turn asked for something he wanted to have better in the coming week. The others each in turn affirmed his request.

"That sounds less intense than the groups I led," notes Space-Holder, "so I can see why your group was able to continue for many months. But what happened recently to upset you so?"

Explorer is so agitated about it that he can hardly find words.

"It was awful," Explorer begins. "In retrospect I saw signs of it coming for the past several weeks. The things I noticed involved the leader's integrity having slipped in little ways. I tried to overlook them and not judge his flaws too harshly. Then today he just came apart at the seams. One minute he was being paranoid and defensive, saying there were spies and evil spirits attacking the group, and the next minute he was demanding our total allegiance to him, even to the point of saying he was such a high spiritual being that we should all worship him. At first the group was split over whether we should go along or not but by the end of the meeting most everyone but the leader could see he was just crazy.

"How can such things happen?," cries Explorer showing the pain of his shattered faith in his group leader.

Space-Holder asks him if he wants to use that as his first question in the question-answer process.

Explorer whimpers, "Maybe I should try to calm my agitation first." He pauses for awhile, gathering himself.

What assumption do I have that is generating my agitation?

That good spiritual people are supposed to be stable and nurturing throughout their lives.

What new assumption would calm me?

God's loving energy is always there. It is available to each individual who is willing to make some transilient good assumptions. This is true even if our human manifestation of God's love doesn't work perfectly to be always spiritually nurturing.

But my individual experience of God's loving energy doesn't seem enough—I need other people to relate to in a spiritual context. So presuming this is true, what is the calming assumption about that?

I can't think of one. It seems like all people are potentially unreliable. And that's not very calming.

What new assumption, if I could make it—even if I can't make it at the moment—would calm me?

I'll always be able to survive such betrayals by an all-too-human spiritual leader, and always be able to find a new one when I need to.

"That feels better," continues Explorer, "but I'm still feeling the embarrassment I felt when the group leader accused me of failing to support him in the group and hurting his feelings. I know that it can be very wounding to a leader not to be supported."

"Do you remember what the formula for how embarrassment is generated that I presented last year?" asks Space-Holder.

"I remember that embarrassment was one of the agitated energies, but I can't remember the assumption that generated it," says Explorer.

Space-Holder repeats the formula: "Embarrassment is generated by the inaccurate attribution of cause in an empathy situation.

"Oh wow, yes, I remember, but I'm not clear on who was the cause for what. How do I figure it out?"

"Not to repeat myself," smiles Space-Holder, "but how about doing the Question-Answer process? It's important to become clear on who's causing whose pain."

Who was causing the group leader's pain?
I can see that I thought I was the cause of his pain, whereas in fact he was at cause for his own pain by making an inaccurate assumption and not being responsible for his own reactions. I see that I am responsible for my own pain of embarrassment by having assumed that I was the cause of his pain. If I assume I didn't do anything wrong, my embarrassment disappears. In that kind of situation I'll have to let the group leader or whoever handle their own.

Space-Holder nodded and asked, "Does that handle all of it?"

"No, the betrayal still hurts a lot. I guess it's too fresh a shock and needs much more time spent in the healing effect of transilient good."

What could I assume now that would enable me to get out of this pain and back to transilient good?

Go through the pain and feel it, asking at each step what assumption is generating it there.

What assumption is generating my immediate pain?

The leader couldn't do such a betraying thing to me when I'm so good and worthy—either I'm not as good as I thought or he's not as good as I thought.

Who should I see as responsible for causing the betrayal?

Who is the perpetrator who did something bad? I didn't do anything bad. I can't be responsible for someone else using his free-will to make some crazy assumptions.

O.K., would it calm me if I assume my ex-group-leader is now in a very unreliable state and that he got there through some unresolved process of his own? Is all I have to do to protect myself to distance enough from him so he can't wound me any longer?

Nope. I'm angry.

What assumption do I have that is generating my anger?

It's two things—he's a malevolent bad guy who pulled the rug out from under me—and I'm angry with myself because as a good person I think should be healing him.

What assumption, if I made it, would calm my anger?

He's a poor mistaken foolish crazy person whom I will no longer let influence me.

What am I feeling now?

An empty loss feeling that I no longer have this spiritual leader to relate to. I wanted an I-thou relationship where we were solid in our integrity and where each experienced each other's unique self.

What am I assuming to be true that is generating this empty feeling?

That if I don't have him to relate to with integrity then I don't experience myself as a crystallized unique self any more.

What new assumption would calm me?

I know I exist. As Moses quoted God saying about God's name: "I am that I am."

"The thought," complains Explorer, "that I will have future spiritual relationships in which I experience myself uniquely doesn't seem to calm me now. It must be a possible good story that hasn't grown yet. I guess I need more healing time soaking in transilient good."

What could I assume that would get me back to experiencing transilient good?

I am that I am. And God knows I am even if no one else does. That seems fine, however I seem to still be worried about my ex-spiritual leader.

Do I still want to heal him?

Yes. If I'm as good a person as I assume I am, shouldn't I be able to heal him?

He has free will to make whatever mistakes he chooses. I need to trust that he is on his own spiritual journey and can potentially learn from this experience. Further, it's all in divine order even if I can't see any order to it at the moment. I need to turn him over to God and let them work it out together.

Shouldn't I offer to help him?

Not unless he asks me and even then only if my inner guidance is that helping him is my job.

"I'm calmed down now," observes Explorer. "But it will be some time before I can trust another spiritual leader like that."

"Have you considered forming your own little spiritual support group?" asks Space-Holder. "One of my old adages is that if you can't find a group you want to join, then create one."

Explorer thinks about this for a time. "Perhaps when I am more healed I will try it. Meantime, thanks for being there for me, sane and stable as usual."

"Anytime," smiled Space-Holder. "It's always easier to maintain integrity in a one-on-one relationship like ours, than as a leader of a group. See what you can do."

Explorer strolls off, deep in thought about both the importance of spiritual groups and their difficulties.

Chapter 18

A Problem with Prayer

Explorer docks his boat and decides to take a stroll along the grass and flower covered slope that leads up from the bank. The air is soft and fragrant. It has been a good spring and new growth is everywhere, yet he can't seem to appreciate it all. As he walks along, he finds Space-Holder sitting on a grassy knoll, reading a book. Explorer greets his old friend in a preoccupied way, and sits down beside him.

"Space-Holder," begins Explorer quietly, "I have a problem with prayer. Maybe it's just that I don't know how to do it right or I haven't practiced enough but I can't seem to create a fulfilling prayer life for myself."

Space-Holder nods and looks off in the distance at the flowers. He turns back to face Explorer and says, "It isn't as simple as it sounds. Try the question-answer process on the problem."

Explorer looks down at the grass for a minute, then begins: "What is my first question?

Why am I having so much difficulty with prayer?

It just isn't easy.

Getting back to basics then, how would I describe what prayer is?

Prayer isn't just talking to oneself. It's talking to someone or something else.

Is this always the way it is?

Yes.

Maybe I don't know who or what I am talking to. Is this prayer problem related directly to my previous problem with God being too diffuse for me to know?

Yes, definitely. But what I learned from that previous session about God (Chapter 15) doesn't solve the problem here. There I learned to make the assumption that God loves me, and to judge whether it was working by whether I felt good energy coming into my experience. That got around the problem of my not knowing who God was because I didn't have to focus on my loving God. This time however if I'm going to talk to God in prayer it seems to me I have to know to whom I am addressing myself.

Do I have to know more about who God is in order to have an effective prayer life?

Analyze more about what prayer is and what results you want from it before you try to answer that question.

What is prayer?

It's either asking someone for something I desire — petitionary prayer—or thanking someone for having already given me what I desired before—giving thanks. It's also something about praising and glorifying —saying how wonderful the person or thing is.

Is this the same as expressing myself about how I love God?

Yes. Not just being grateful for the wonderful things God has done for me but also my giving expression to an overflow of loving feelings for God, which also seems to require knowing who God is.

Who is God?

He is the source of the loving and enlivening feelings I experience coming into me.

Do I know anything more about God than that?

Only that he is the source of the energy that creates all the good in the world.

Do I know anything else about God?

Only that no one else seems to know God as a unique being any better than I do.

Is this much knowledge about God enough for me to know whom I am addressing my prayers?

It doesn't seem to have been.

What results from praying have I been looking for?

Having in my life a clean, clear, well grounded, regularly performed communication from me to God —and in the presence of whom I can center my spiritual existence.

Do I need any response from God for this communication to be complete—other than the above mentioned experience of good loving energy coming in to me?

Yes. I need an experience of glory—that's the only word I can think of to call it.

What do I imagine this experience of glory to be like?

All golden light and of higher order spiritual things.

Is this what I really have been missing and desiring and longing for in my dissatisfaction with my prayer life?

Yes, absolutely—having an experience of glory would enable me to know I was doing prayer right.

Is the experience of glory more important than an experience of a verbal dialogue with God in which to be grounded spiritually?

No. Both are important and essential.

Are they generated by different aspects of the prayer process?

Yes, opposite aspects. The verbal dialogue is transfixed and grounded in transfixing assumptions such as knowing God, just as the healing process for battered reality is transfixed. The glory experience is generated by transilient assumptions—just as the healing-of-good process is. Examples of those kinds of transilient assumptions occur in spiritual literature as "praising God and glorifying him forever."

Do these two types of processes need to have separate distinct places in the prayer?

Yes, definitely. They fulfill two different functions. When you're doing one, you're not doing the other. Each in turn needs to have its place and form.

Can I trust that the answers from God that come up in my dialogue experience during the transfixed part—the "knowing God part"—are accurate enough? Can I assume they really are from God and are accurately enough clothed in words I can understand?

The criterion here is whether the prayer dialogue is working. Ask yourself whether it is generating a clear nurturing identity for God. If it isn't, review your assumptions about God and correct them until the desired result is achieved. Trust the principle that if you are receiving it accurately God is always nurturing.

Aren't there potential circumstances in which God's responses would need to be stern and judgmental of me?

No. That's not God's function. He lets the hard lessons be taught by circumstances in the world. His direct contribution is always nurturing and supportive to the praying person. That's because a person's inner experience of God is only from God as the force for good. God as co-creator of the physical world already put limits on hell ('The fixed pains of hell,' to quote C. S. Lewis' poem[7]—it's his mercy that lets it only get so bad. Our experience of agitation and pain are our encounters with that structured (transfixed) aspect of the world. It is fully firm and solid, so when God manifests in our inner experience as the force for good, we always experience it as gently loving and nurturing (transilient).

How about those instances of intense energy?

They are the gentlest God can be and get the job done.

But some people have hellish inner experiences. Where do they come from?

Not from God—at least not directly from God. They come from the person's inaccurate assumptions encountering God's truth and reality. It is the best God can do to get their attention to the errors in their freely made assumptions. God is trying to motivate the person to rectify the errors.

All right so if I can trust the answers I get—or if I correct my assumptions until I get nurturing answers in the part of my prayer dialogue that is about the things of the world—how do I generate the glory part?

Go back to transilient assumptions.

What transilient assumptions can I make that will generate in me an experience of glory?

Poetic things—in the mystery, as opposed to the knowingness of the earlier part of the prayer. I can write or spontaneously make up my own poetry or read other writers poems.

If I were going to write some poetry right now that would generate an experience of glory—what would it be?

Heroic comes from ancient lands,
The one whose noble mind and fiery spirit
Will give our mundane world
The hope and vision clear

151

To guide our way home,
Where we are missed and long past due.

Does that give me an experience of glory?

Yes, wonderfully.

Is that similar to the messiah tales told in the Old Testament or the second coming story about Jesus or the mystic fool that Charles Williams writes about in The Greater Trumps?[8]

Perhaps, but the important thing is that the old religious tales don't do it for me right now and this little poetry I wrote does.

Can generating glory be overdone?

Not as long as a person stays grounded and functional in the other roles.

Space-Holder reaches over to his pack and extracts two charts, one showing the six roles (Table V) and the other showing way we experience God in each of the six roles (Table VII). (See the tables at the end of the chapter.) "I'm going to cover some intricate, seemingly complicated, but powerful ways of viewing our relationship with God. You may not get it all on the first hearing, but periodically review what I'm going to describe—experiment with it and it will sink in.

"There are three ways," he begins," of experiencing God as a knowing being who expresses himself in words. The first one—and it bears on the glory you are talking about—is usually generated by the person being in Role 2 and experiencing God in the opposite role, Role 1. In Role 2 the person is a unique individual striving to survive. He opens himself to an experience of God through the transilient assumptions of this role—in this case being in mystery rather than knowing everything, and being in the good of the present moment rather than in the past and future of a good story.

"The general rule is that the person experiences God *through* the transilient assumptions of the role the person is in, but the particular form of God which he experiences is God *being in the opposite role*—the role in which all the transfixed assumptions become transilient, and vice versa. This comes about because the person and God naturally complement each other—when the person takes the positions of one particular role, from his viewpoint he sees God automatically fill in the opposite leftover positions.

"In this case the person in Role 2 experiences God as a Role 1 Healer/Myth Maker communicating in poetry. God is speaking from being both knowing and in a good story, an eternal being in empathy with all. To experience God directly in this classically glorious form is very energizing to our spirits and results in what you call an experience of glory.

"It is useful to contrast this experience of God with those generated in the other roles. Earlier today you were speaking of a more transfixed experience of God in which you could be in mystery while writing down a sort of letter which God would be dictating to you. This is the second example of God being verbal and knowing. It usually happens when God is knowing and striving in Role 3 and you are in the opposite—Role 4—being a unique individual in a good story. Such a letter can give you clarification about God's perspective on your good story—a type of communication most of us hunger for. It validates the reality of our good story which is very useful, but doesn't give us the experience of glory obtained in the previous example.

"The third example of God in a knowing role would be where God is in Role 6, a unique individual knowing being who sheds the intuitive knowledge received in the question-answer process by a person who is in mystery and empathy as a Nurturer/Protector in Role 5.

"In the other three roles, God is in mystery, so his communications do not come through in words. If we start by switching sides in the last example, the person goes into being a unique knowing individual who experiences God through the transilient assumptions of Role 6—being an eternal being in the transilient good of the present moment. He experiences God as the nurturing golden energy that infuses him occasionally. You have previously spoken of such experiences happening in that hypnogogic state just after your waking when it is particularly easy to assume that one is a safe eternal being in the moment.

"To continue to switch sides, if the person is knowing and striving in the workaday world in Role 3 he would experience God through the transilient assumptions of being in empathy with all and in the transilient good of the present moment. God would appear to be in Role 4, a unique being in a good story, raining love on the whole world—in contrast to the golden energy that was raining love on the one individual in the previous example. This "love-rain" would be experienced as the beauty shining in the whole world that inspires the person in his work.

"In the final example, the person shifts into Role 1 as an eternal knowing being sharing with his kin a good story. He experiences God as existing in Role 2, shining through the eyes of the unique individual being of his significant other who is striving in the world. In this role he can see the perfect divine core of any person he loves—which is very healing for all concerned."

Explorer is impressed by the ability of this system to delineate all these various ways that God has been experienced by people. His attention is especially caught by the last example since he has long wished that he could learn how to skillfully operate in Role 1 as a Healer/Myth Maker.

"When do I learn how to do Role 1?" Explorer asks.

Space-Holder recommends he look at it in his own question-answer process. Explorer continues:

When do I learn to do Role 1?
When I can tell a story to my kin about goodness that is true or about truth that is good.

So what then is the format of my prayer process that I want to experiment with?

God asks me what I want and I go inside for a current answer—not my list from yesterday. Then I ask God what he wants. Then I draw on some poetry that generates an experience of the glory.

Should I try it now?

Yes.

God: What do you want, Explorer?

Explorer: I want to feel my life isn't a failure.

God: You've never used the world's criteria for success. What is your assumption generating your sense of failure now?

Explorer: That eventually I should have gotten it all together in my life.

God: What new assumption would enable you to feel calm?

Explorer: That this is it—my life is what it is in this moment right now. My life is—it exists—what exists is good—so my life is good.

Explorer: What do you God want to say to me?

God: I love you and I want you well. Stay in contact with my love until you feel healed.

Explorer: I really want to do that, but sometimes I'll get distracted.

God: What is your poetry to generate glory?

Explorer: I will use a poem I wrote some time ago:

The end is in the middle,
The last is always first.
There is no hoping without longing,
There is no loving without pain.
Give me your heart that I may break it,
And release the butterfly spirit within.
The spirit trapped in your heart

Is longing for the return to the light.
Let it fly.
It will do you no good trapped.
There is gold in the diamond if the sparkle dies.
Break your heart and let the liquid love
Turn your night into day, your lost into found.
Give me your broken heart
And I will show you the mysteries of a thousand
worlds.

God: Does it give you an experience of glory?

Explorer: Most certainly. Many thanks and Amen.

The moment seems magical to both of the men. The spring air wafts silently across the slope, ruffling the flowers in waves. Space-Holder turns to his friend and nods in approval. He slowly returns the charts to his pack. Explorer stands, smiles and goes off to practice his new prayer life.

TABLE V

Six Balanced Roles in Life

ROLE NUMBERS AND NAMES	TRANSFIXING ASSUMPTIONS (Structured)	TRANSILIENT ASSUMPTIONS (Energizing)
1: HEALER— MYTH MAKER	Knowing + In a Good Story	In Kinship + Relaxing in Safety
2: THRILL SEEKER— SPORTSMAN	Striving + A Unique Individual	In Mystery + Just Being Now
3: CRAFTSMAN— SCIENTIST	Knowing + Striving	In Kinship + Just Being Now
4: ROMANTIC— ARTIST	A Unique Individual + In a Good Story	In Mystery + Relaxing in Safety
5: NURTURER— PROTECTOR	Striving + In a Good Story	In Mystery + In Kinship
6: THEORETICIAN— DETECTIVE	Knowing + A Unique Individual	Relaxing in Safety + Just Being Now

TABLE VII

Experience of God in Six Roles

ROLE I AM IN	ROLE GOD IS IN	FORM I EXPERIENCE GOD IN
Role 2 *Thrill Seeker— Sportsman*	**Role 1** *Healer— Myth Maker*	Poetry. Myth. Truth about Goodness. Goodness about Truth.
Role 4 *Romantic— Artist*	**Role 3** *Craftsman— Scientist*	Straight-talking letter about my good story.
Role 5 *Nurturer— Protector*	**Role 6** *Theoretician— Detective*	Truth rain. Intuitive knowledge in unique packets in Q-A process.
Role 6 *Theoretician— Detective*	**Role 5** *Nurturer— Protector*	Nurturing golden energy experience within a unique individual person.
Role 3 *Craftsman— Scientist*	**Role 4** *Romantic— Artist*	Love rain on whole external world seen as beauty of the world.
Role 1 *Healer— Myth Maker*	**Role 2** *Thrill Seeker— Sportsman*	Divine core of my beloved significant other, and all unique physical beings.

Chapter 19

Difficulties After Having Been Nurturing

Explorer returns again to Space-Holder's grassy knoll carrying an arm load of family photograph albums. He sits down with a bewildered look on his face and reveals his problem.

"I've been looking in these old family photo albums, trying to find out the answers to who I am or who I was or what happened to me. I've been nurturing my family for many years and I seem to have lost who I am in the process. I would like to discover who I really am, and then see that reflection of myself in these pictures at various times in my life.

Space-Holder nods sympathetically, and points out, "Being nurturing is done in Role 5 where you are in the empathy mode. You work hard creating a good supportive atmosphere for your family members, which is a noble endeavor. However, being in all that empathy does tend to cloud the issue of who you are as a unique individual. Why don't you try some question-answer process on the problem."

Explorer settles down to see if he can shed any light on his confusion.

Who in me wants to know who I am?

I do.

What part of me are you?

I'm the part that is a unique individual and I can't seem to find myself during much of this life.

You seem to know clearly who you are at this point, so what exactly is the problem?

My uniqueness seems to get lost during all these nurturing times.

Is the problem that you didn't get enough times to express yourself?

If these albums are the record of our life, I'm not visible anywhere.

Where were you while all this nurturing was going on?

I guess I was standing in the wings letting you do this nurturing empathy number.

Was standing in the wings boring or a problem for you?

Neither. I understood the situation. An empathy role is much better for family relationships—but I'm not in the play. There was no one encouraging me to be an individual in my own right.

I did the best I could to give you a chance to play and think fun thoughts and figure out fun theories. Did you appreciate that?

Yes, absolutely. I really enjoyed those times but it was all on a mental plane. When do I get my turn to act on the physical plane as a unique individual?

Could you trust anyone to make that possible for you?

I do seem to have a fear about that.

What is your assumption generating this fear?

There is no one that I can trust to be really support-ing of me when I'm being this unique individual self.

Is your unique self an especially difficult, abrasive or obnoxious type of person who would be a real challenge to support?

we know enough and can learn more fast enough to handle our present-life situation. After all, we are not living in times when any group of people have developed this knowledge very highly as yet. Maybe our sense of integrity will keep enough ahead of this developing knowledge this time, so that we can use it wisely instead of for destruction. That is a potential good story which is still too hard for me to make now, but I can abide in the nurturing energies of transilient good in the meantime.

So, referring back to your original problem, do you still feel that you are too hard a case to be nurtured by anyone?

No. I'm all right now. I guess it would be hard for any human to compensate for someone not having nurturing energy coming to them from transilient good. Both sources of good are needed—neither source can do it by itself. The psychic good energy isn't enough without the nurturer and vice versa.

When I was being the nurturer in my family, were the other members also receiving transilient good energy from within themselves?

It worked didn't it? So they must have been. They weren't involved in my original past life assumption that made transilient good unavailable to me, so they have been able to let in some good energy.

Space-Holder asks, "Does that handle your original problem—not being able to find yourself in your life?"

Explorer responds, "Yes, it let me know where I was instead. And why and how I don't have to do that any more. When I see myself looking burned out in my family photos, I know that this happened. It was true just because I didn't have the nurturing energy coming from transilient good assumptions. Now I know how to be uniquely me and nurtured in myself."

Chapter 20

Untamed Parts of Self

Explorer has been noticing for a long time that angry feelings would arise for no particular reason. When he would be relaxed and ask himself what he wanted to do for fun, the answer would come up "kill people." He could not understand why this extreme reaction should continue to happen. Today, he is dedicating himself to working on it. He knows it may take a long time, and he is willing to put in as much time and energy as it takes. He finds Space-Holder sitting on his grassy knoll and joins him.

After explaining the problem Explorer asks, "Isn't there a different way to handle my anger?"

Space-Holder responds, "Find the assumption generating it, and clear it with a new calming one."

Explorer shifts around to get comfortable, then moves into his question-answer process:

What assumption do I have that is generating my anger?
Words of anger immediately come up:
'You S.O.B!'
'I am going to get you.'
'You did this to me and I am going to make you pay.' 'You are a son-of-a-bitch.'
'I am going to get you.'
'I am going to get you. There's no way you can avoid me. I am your worst nightmare, and I will be with you always. I am going to haunt you into an

early grave. You are the worst person in the world. I hate you with a venom that has no end. I will get you for this if it takes my whole life. I will never give up. I will never relent. You are mine and I will squeeze the life out of you.'

Will you talk to me?

There is nothing to say. Only venom.

It would help if you would talk to me so I could figure out what you are so angry about and maybe figure out something else to do about it. Will you talk to me?

There is no hope for justice. There is no power great enough to give me justice. I have to vindicate this myself.

Will you tell me what happened that got you so angry?

There is no way to heal this. It is beyond redemption. There is no use looking at it because there is nothing that can be done about it.

Two heads are better than one. Do you think I could understand it if you described it to me?

No. No one could understand it.

Are you human?

Yes, barely.

Are you myself in a previous incarnation, a past life?

Yes.

I am human too so maybe I could understand it. Will you tell me what happened?

You have not been through what I have.

Tell me about it. Maybe I could relate to it at least in some degree.

They stuck me in this dungeon for years and years. A black mucky stinking hole. They throw down enough bread to keep me alive, and I am too hungry not to eat it. There is no drain. I have to sit in my own urine and feces all the time. They give me rags enough to keep me from freezing to death. The only light is a chink from above. There is no way out but death.

Why are they doing this to you?

They have long since forgotten the original reason that they put me here— an unwanted child that then became the scapegoat of the community. No one could be worse off than me—an animal in a cage of my own filth. They don't even talk to me like a real person. They think I never learned how to speak their language. I have only one little hope or joy. Once before they put me in here I saw a glowing picture of the Madonna. I know she exists somewhere in the universe. When I finish venting my anger on those who did this to me I will go searching for her. When I find her all will be well. She will love me and I will serve her forever. But first I have to get these people who did this to me. It is only my anger that keeps me alive. I would have given up in despair long ago if it were not for my anger.

How did you finally die? Can you come up to the time of your death in that lifetime?

No. I don't want to. I want to hang on to what life I have and it is totally dedicated to getting those people.

But in order to haunt them and get them don't you have to die first?

No. If I die I may go unconscious and forget my anger. I must never forget my anger. I must keep my body alive so I don't forget my anger. I can get them psychically even while I am alive. I can make their lives totally miserable. They will have lifetime after lifetime of me making them miserable. I must never let myself forget my anger. I have to figure out how to take it with me after I die.

Since you still have your anger and I am experiencing you from another lifetime, it seems like you successfully accomplished taking your anger with you after you died didn't you?

Yes and I am never letting it go.

Isn't it true that no one can make you let it go?

Yes. I have free will about this and I'm never ever letting go of my anger.

I think you deserve to keep your anger if you choose but isn't it keeping you miserable long after you needed to be?

I knew you would try to talk me out of my anger. Why do you think I have refused to talk to you before?

In the past I have just kept you around as a tool—a weapon to point when I needed some anger. Nothing could stand up to you. You have been a very powerful tool for me. But isn't there some better way to handle this?

No! I am not letting you talk me out of this. I need to have this anger in me all the time.

If I could show you how you could generate anger whenever you wanted to—by making an anger-generating assumption—would you be willing to sometimes do something else?

No. I always want to be angry.

At this point, Explorer decides to try some healing imagery. He creates an image that the angry person is still alive; in this fantasy, Explorer imagines the group that did the perpetrations as having matured over the centuries and now wants to heal the angry person. He creates an image that the group has available to them all the knowledge and resources of the present-day world.

The group, in Explorer's fantasy, gradually changes the angry person's surroundings. First they give him a slop bucket that can be emptied twice a day, plus tools to clean up his hole. They introduce more light from above, better clothes, warm bedding, and better food. They let people occasionally talk to him from the top of the hole, being nice to him this time. He won't be able to be nice at first. He will still have his anger. They can try to explain to him that they want to let him out of the hole, but they can't let him roam free until he is able to behave himself appropriately. If he goes around venting his anger on people, maiming and killing, they can't let him out.

First, they build a cage up on the surface level that has access to the hole. The cage is set up so he can live in it if he chooses. They finally put a ladder into the hole so he can climb up and down from the cage to the hole and back when he wants to. More people talk to him while he is up in the cage; they try to get him to relate to them in a nice friendly way. So far he is still too angry to do so, but comfortable living helps him to mellow a little.

Then, they install a motherly-type volunteer to live next to the cage. She tries to act in a nurturing way toward him, but she still can't touch him through the cage bars because he is still angry enough to be dangerous. He accepts her presence gradually, but still refuses to engage in a real conversation. This pattern continues for a long time.

They try to civilize him with pets, first introducing a dog into his cage, but he is still so angry that he just kills several dogs. They give up on that idea.

Then they add more people to the area, though still outside the cage. They add children to be like a family with the mother, a school room where he can learn with the children, a bar where he can see how men relate to each other, a TV with various sports and entertainment shows. He is still angry, but he is getting more educated. One day he finally asks a question:

Why did you people change the way you were treating me?

We didn't believe it could be that bad for you in the hole. We believed—we hate to admit it—that you were really not human and didn't sense things or notice things the way a human would. Then over the years and centuries—over many lifetimes—we gradually learned and became aware that you were human too just like us. Gradually more of us felt bad for being so mean to you. But it took a long time for the consensus of the culture to decide it was time to do something different about you. Then it has taken a still longer time to figure out what to do about you—how to heal you without jeopardizing the safety of the rest of us. We knew how angry you were and that you would destroy us if we gave you the chance before you were healed.

That doesn't seem good enough to make up for all the years in the black hole. You all just want to be nice and make up but I still want revenge and I'm going to get it if it is the last thing I do. And I know you people! The first sign of stress and you will be wanting to put me or anyone like me back in the black hole again. You are still primitives underneath that veneer of civilization. There is no way I would trust you again—even a little bit. (He cannot find another question with which to continue the process.)

After that, the personage retreated back to the hole again. He spent some time recalling the bad old days when he was cold and filthy and starving there.

He had become smarter and more educated, but now he also wanted to get stronger physically. He demanded exercise equipment with which he could work out. The others were at first somewhat afraid to let him get physically stronger, for fear he would be even harder to control if they ever let him out of the cage. However, some pointed out that he was already almost maximally dangerous. It was his psyche that would have to be healed before he could be trusted out of his cage, and perhaps becoming fit physically would help heal his psyche.

So they continued this pattern for quite a long time. Finally, he became well enough and mature enough for his hormones to become active. He began having sex dreams and masturbating, and finally fell in love with one of the girls on the outside of the cage.

At first, he was shy about communicating this to her. Eventually, he got up the courage and wrote her a little note that he slipped to her through the bars. As usual in the course of human events, this course of love did not run smoothly. He got his feelings hurt. In fact, he hurt so much from her rejection that for a time he thought more about this pain than about his old anger.

In time, he healed enough to try it again with other young women, falling in and out of love regularly, still with a lot of pain each time. Gradually, he matured in this process, and finally he fell in love with someone who returned his love. She wanted to get him out of the cage so she could marry him. This confronted the community with the problem of how they were going to tell if he had healed enough to be trusted out of his cage.

He told them that he was still angry underneath, and he would dedicate himself to working more on that area eventually, but his love was now stronger than his anger. He swore that he would never act on his impulses for revenge and his desire to hurt people. He wanted to get his chance to live in the world like other people, to marry, to have children and to have a loving family life. He would never hurt his beloved fiancee nor his future family nor any of the community. However, if the community needed someone to fight against invaders or other bad people, he was their man. His old anger was an energy that would prove useful there.

They put their faith in him and let him out of the cage. At first they let him out for just a few minutes, then for some hours, but finally altogether. For many years he was a peaceful, law-abiding citizen. However, he remained a little aloof from the community. He knew he was different from them. For one thing, he was the best fighter when they needed someone to fight for them.

He seemed to have an endless supply of hostile energy which he could focus on an enemy. For another thing, he had greater empathy than others for the plight of the downtrodden. He asked various authorities, counselors, and priests, what he could do about his anger, but none of them had any constructive ideas. Nor did they have the time to listen to him fruitlessly moan and groan about his old life. He felt that he could go on and on talking about it forever, but no one wanted to listen.

Finally, at Explorer's request, he is willing to do his own question-answer process, with Explorer supporting him unconditionally as long as he doesn't hurt anyone. His first question is:

Why did all those people do such things to me?

They responded to their own traumatic events by feeling that they had to lash out at someone who was weaker and more vulnerable. They took out their hurt and pain and anger on me, as a victim and scapegoat.

Why did those people change their minds and provide for my recovery process? Why were they nice and giving me what I needed to rehabilitate myself into a functional member of society—albeit they don't realize I still want to kill everyone though I don't act on it?

They changed because they got enlightened. They wanted to make amends for their previous bad treatment of me.

How did I die in that lifetime and what assumptions did I make at that time?

I died in the pit. But I survived much longer by being so angry.

Was it worth it to use the energy of the anger to survive longer?

Not particularly. However, I felt that I would lose myself if I didn't keep up the anger and keep intending to handle such perpetrators by killing everyone.

Did I feel my soul would die if I didn't maintain my anger, even after death?

Yes. I felt that I personally had to handle this evil in the world by killing everybody and cleansing the place of the human race. Otherwise I was a wimpy nothing—a nobody who wasn't taking adequate responsibility to handle evil. If I didn't continue to intend to handle it, I would lose my integrity.

Is it really possible that as in the self-as-source philosophy, my soul—my essential identity—the real being I am who makes assumptions and creates my reality at any given time, and who is aware of experience as it arises—that this self of mine is of a higher order of reality? Higher than any assumptions or experience—higher than any events or circumstances in life? A higher order of reality that would not disappear and my integrity would remain intact even if I let go of this assumption that I needed to kill everybody in retaliation for the black hole lifetime?

Yes, that is the point. That's the fact that would enable me to let go of the assumption that is generating my anger.

What would be my new calming assumption?

That the unique identity I am defending in my Role 2-survival-is-threatened-assumption is not the same as my basic soul identity which is invulnerable to any of the circumstances and events of life.

Would the identity of my soul survive even such a destructive process as could be wielded by evil people who might be in control of powerful psychic energies?

Yes. This eternal soul that I am would survive even though my physical body died. I would still be free to reincarnate again.

To repeat the question, can I as the man in the black pit trust that my essential soul—its identity, and integrity—is totally safe and invulnerable always so that I don't have to preserve this anger-generating assumption even in these most awful circumstances?

Yes, my soul is safe.

If I had assumed that in the black hole how would the experience have been different for me?

I probably would have dissociated and had experiences of transilient good which would have nurtured my soul though my body might have died sooner without the anger and its agitated energy. That would have been all right—living longer in that life was no big advantage to anyone.

Can I make this new assumption now?

I am testing it out and seeing what other issues—if any—it brings up.

How is this relevant to people suffering with multiple personality disorder?

The same process would apply to them. They would need to have each alter remember the assumption it had made that is defending its separate identity and change to trusting in the senior reality of its essential soul. This would not be as simple as it sounds. It would take an extensive amount of time and therapy to arrive at a clear experience of the defensive assumption that requires changing. However, it is basically the same principle.

Explorer now shifts to doing his own question-answer process. He asks:

Explorer now shifts to doing his own question-answer process. He asks:

Can I, Explorer, now experience having fun adventures in Role 2 without having to handle the anger and revenge feelings from the person I was in the black hole?

Yes, absolutely. I should go and have a good time adventuring.

Space-Holder grins in appreciation of the wonderful job Explorer has done. "You have uncovered the key assumption that enabled you to resolve the anger that had been coming up unbidden. You're going to have wonderful adventures," he chortles, "in the new freedom and energy you now have available."

Explorer lets out a "yahoo", bear-hugs Space-Holder until he can hardly breathe. Then, Explorer runs off gleefully toward his boat, kicking his heels in the air in anticipation of the adventures ahead. ☐

Footnotes

[1]est training

[2]Lewis, C.S., 1946, *The Great Divorce,* New York: The Macmillan Company, Pages 120-121

[3]Savary, L. and Berne, P., 1988, *Kything - The Art of Spiritual Presence,* New York and Mahwah, N.J.: Paulist Press, P. 24

[4]Although this chapter continues to use the universal masculine pronouns of the allegory, it is clarifying for the reader to realize it was written by a female author about her experience of the male manifestation of God. In other settings, such as her counseling role, she has often successfully coached males working on their relationship with God to experience the female manifestation of God, calling her variously, "The Female Power of The Universe", or "The Divine Woman Within."

[5]Friedman, Maurice, Fall 1972, Dialogue and The Unique in Humanistic Psychology. *Journal of Humanistic Psychology,* 12:7-22

[6]Spiegel, M.D., David, 1993, *Living Beyond Limits,* New York, Ballantine Books

[7]Lewis, C.S., 1933, 1943, *The Pilgrim's Regress,* Grand Rapids: Wm B. Eerdmans Publishing Co., P. 180

[8]Williams, Charles, 1932, 1950, *The Greater Trumps,* Grand Rapids: Wm. Eerdmans Publishing Co.

Appendix

Tables:

Glossary of Terms

History of the Development of Willowbrook Philosophy

About the Author

My Poems from God

TABLE I

Steps of the Question-Answer Process

Step One: Get a Question

Notice something you are curious about and form a specific question about it.

Step Two: I Don't Know

Let go into an experience of "I don't know." Don't try to figure it out logically.

Step Three: An Answer

Notice the next experience that comes up. It may be words in your mind's ear, or pictures in your mind's eye, or an emotion, or a sensation in your body. If "I don't know" is what comes up, look at the next thing which comes up after that in your experience.

Step Four: Assume the Answer to be True

Put whatever came up in Step 3 into words, and for the moment, assume it to be the true answer to the question. If the answer in Step 3 were true, what would be your next question? Go on repeating the four steps until there is some clarity about the area of the questions. Then step back and decide what assumption to experimentally assume to be true for the next few days.

TABLE II

Possible Sources of Answers

1 . One's own personal mental computer, including memories of experiences and a stack of operating assumptions.

2 . Universal mental computer, also called by some the Akashic Record or "Mind", having been defined as the "multi-sensory, linear, recorded instants of now."[1]

3 . Extrasensory perception (e.s.p.) of another incarnate person's personal mental computer.

4 . Extrasensory perception of a discarnate person's mental computer.

5 . One's Higher Self, or Soul, or God, or All-knowing Wisdom.

6 . Higher beings who are fellow travelers on our path. Examples include: Angels, Moses, Jesus, Buddha, Mary, Gabriel, guides.

TABLE III

Pairs of Transfixing and Transilient Assumptions About Myself

("I am . . .)

ASPECTS OF ME	TRANSFIXING ASSUMPTIONS	TRANSILIENT ASSUMPTIONS
MIND	*. . . Knowing"*	*. . . In Mystery"*
	I live in a knowable world where it's possible to figure out anything.	I live in a mysterious, wondrous universe, unknowable in its entirety.
SPIRIT	*. . . Uniquely Individual"*	*. . . In Empathy & Kinship"*
	I am a unique, separate, individual, viable being.	I am one with all, in empathy and kinship with all creation.
BODY	*. . . Striving"*	*. . . Relaxing in Safety"*
	I need to strive hard to survive and succeed in this physical world.	I am relaxed and trust that my existence is supported by the eternal universe.
EMOTIONS	*. . . In a Good Story"*	*. . . Just Being Now"*
	I focus on my vision of the future good which is better than what is now.	All the good that exists is present in this moment and available if I open to it.

TABLE IV

Symptoms from Over-Running an Assumption

The conditions which result from using an assumption beyond the time it is effective.

ASPECTS OF ME	OVERRUN ASSUMPTIONS	SYMPTOMS RESULTING FROM OVERRUN	ASSUMPTION TO MAKE FOR HEALING
MIND	Knowing	*Dogmatic*	In Mystery
	In Mystery	*In a Battered Reality*	Knowing
SPIRIT	Uniquely Individual	*Isolated and Numb*	In Empathy & Kinship
	In Empathy & Kinship	*Having Fuzzy Ego Boundaries*	Uniquely Individual
BODY	Striving	*Defensively Compulsive*	Relaxing in Safety
	Relaxing in Safety	*Unable to Sustain an Intention*	Striving
EMOTIONS	In a Good Story	*In a Shattered Good Story*	Just Being Now
	Just Being Now	*Drifting Without Goals*	In a Good Story

TABLE V

Six Balanced Roles in Life

ROLE NUMBERS AND NAMES	TRANSFIXING ASSUMPTIONS (Structured)	TRANSILIENT ASSUMPTIONS (Energizing)
1: HEALER— MYTH MAKER	Knowing + In a Good Story	In Kinship + Relaxing in Safety
2: THRILL SEEKER— SPORTSMAN	Striving + A Unique Individual	In Mystery + Just Being Now
3: CRAFTSMAN— SCIENTIST	Knowing + Striving	In Kinship + Just Being Now
4: ROMANTIC— ARTIST	A Unique Individual + In a Good Story	In Mystery + Relaxing in Safety
5: NURTURER— PROTECTOR	Striving + In a Good Story	In Mystery + In Kinship
6: THEORETICIAN— DETECTIVE	Knowing + A Unique Individual	Relaxing in Safety + Just Being Now

TABLE VI

Four Types of Lies Causing a Battered Reality

TYPE OF LIE USED BY THE BATTERING PERSON	DESCRIPTION OF THE LIE	PATHOLOGICAL CONCLUSIONS BY THE BATTERED PERSON
FALSEHOOD	Incorrect description of what actually happened.	"I am wrong"
FALSE BLAME	Incorrect attribution of the cause of what actually happened.	"I am to blame"
PUT-DOWNS	Incorrect description of the other person's essential worthiness. Name-calling. Hateful, vicious and sarcastic tones.	"I am worthless"
EVASIONS	Inadequate feedback about what is true; deliberately fogging the issue; silence; absences.	"I am crazy"

TABLE VI

Continued

TYPE OF LIE USED BY THE BATTERING PERSON	HEALING ASSUMPTIONS
FALSEHOOD	You are deliberately lying to me. I have to wall myself off against you and not let my concepts of reality be affected by what you say. I cancel your vote.
FALSE BLAME	You are 100% responsible for any of your actions. If you did it, you are to blame. If your life did not turn out right, you did not do it right. I put the responsibility for your life on you, and for my life on me.
PUT-DOWNS	You are being a bad person for saying that I am unworthy. As long as I am honest and have basic integrity, I am me and that is not a matter of right or wrong. Being me is the most solid and worthy thing I know.
EVASIONS	You are deliberately trying to prevent me from having a clear experience of what is true, and that is a very mean thing to do. I will assume to be true whatever my current best data tells me is true, and I will act on those assumptions. If you continue to evade me, we can no longer have a partnership of equals, and I have to distance myself from you.

TABLE VII

Experience of God in Six Roles

ROLE I AM IN	ROLE GOD IS IN	FORM I EXPERIENCE GOD IN
Role 2 *Thrill Seeker—Sportsman*	**Role 1** *Healer—Myth Maker*	Poetry. Myth. Truth about Goodness. Goodness about Truth.
Role 4 *Romantic—Artist*	**Role 3** *Craftsman—Scientist*	Straight-talking letter about my good story.
Role 5 *Nurturer—Protector*	**Role 6** *Theoretician—Detective*	Truth rain. Intuitive knowledge in unique packets in Q-A process.
Role 6 *Theoretician—Detective*	**Role 5** *Nurturer—Protector*	Nurturing golden energy experience within a unique individual person.
Role 3 *Craftsman—Scientist*	**Role 4** *Romantic—Artist*	Love rain on whole external world seen as beauty of the world.
Role 1 *Healer—Myth Maker*	**Role 2** *Thrill Seeker—Sportsman*	Divine core of my beloved significant other, and all unique physical beings.

Glossary of Terms

AGITATED ENERGY: A disturbing personal experience of moving or shaking emotions, such as fear, anger, or sadness.

ALTAR: A sacred place consecrated to devotional observances; a central point of worship.

ALTER (ALTER EGO): Another (alternative) aspect of one's own nature, either pathological or not.

ANXIETY: Fearfulness; an example of agitated energy.

ASSUMPTION: A statement which in the past has been, or in the future may be, stipulated and held as true in one's personal view of reality. When so stipulated, one's actions follow as if it were true.

BALANCED ROLE: Functioning in a manner that demonstrates a balance between structuring beliefs (transfixedness) and beliefs that allow open spontaneity (transilience). See Table V for six examples.

BATTERED REALITY: One's sense of what is factually true, which has been assaulted or violated by an event that was beyond belief or by villainous lies. Types of lies include falsehoods, false blame, aspersions about one's worthiness, or lack of data from evasion or silence. Symptoms of a battered reality include agitation, confusion and an inability to know what is true.

BURNOUT: Failure in functioning or achieving desired outcome caused by prolonged expenditure of intense emotional energy toward a desired goal, without replenishing the energy. This energy can be replenished by discontinuing attention on the future goal—being in the present moment and opening to its nurturing spiritual energies (transilient good).

CALM: An inner experience of peace; quiet; stillness; motionless; smoothness (in terms of the "boat" metaphor, not stormy or windy).

COGNITIVE THERAPY: A type of psychological treatment in which emphasis is placed on ferreting out dysfunctional beliefs or assumptions, and working to change them.

COMPLEMENTARY CONTRARIES: A pair of assumptions about reality which are opposite, yet each of which is required at times in various circumstances, to enable one to function best.

DEPRESSION: An emotional condition of very low nurturing energy in the presence of either high amounts of agitated energy (sadness, fear and/or anger), or emotional numbness.

EMBARRASSMENT: A feeling of shame or chagrin caused by the inaccurate attribution of cause in the situation where one is in empathy with another person (healed by accurately assuming the other person is at cause for their own discomfort—see Chapter 17).

EMPATHY: Compassionately putting oneself in another's position and feeling something of what the other feels.

ENERGY: A vibrant inner experience of vitality, power, and aliveness in present time. It may also exist in walled-off pockets, isolated outside of present time, where it was encapsulated by a person when a trauma was too overwhelming to experience fully at the time. These pockets of energy act as stumbling blocks to the free flow of living and may be dissolved by bringing them back into present time in imagination, and living them through to a calm resolution.

ETERNAL: Independent of time; beyond time; always existing.

EVIL: Harmful behavior, attitude or atmosphere arising from a condition for which the perpetrator can be held responsible, such as inaccurate assumptions about basic goodness of self that generate covert defensiveness.

EXPERIENCE: What is perceived, seen, done, felt, or lived through.

EXPLORER: A person who travels through life seeking truth and experience.

FLAILING: Behavior which may inflict harm inadvertently, but for which the perpetrator cannot be held responsible, such as panic in a person with accurate assumptions about goodness of self.

FORCE FOR GOOD: An active power or energy for benefit.

FRACTURED REALITY: A personal belief structure about what is true which has been assaulted or violated by an event that was beyond belief or by villainous lies. Similar to a battered reality.

FUZZY EGO BOUNDARIES: A condition of not having a clearly delineated and understood demarcation between one's self and others.

GOD: The absolute good source of energy. This energy can be experienced in various ways (see Table VII for six examples), pleasant or unpleasant, nurturing or agitating, but ultimately manifests as the highest good for all concerned.

GOOD INTENTIONS PROCESS: The development of the point of view from which one would have volunteered for all the circumstances and events of one's life for a particular beneficial reason. Possible reasons include thinking someone needed loving, something needed learning or demonstration to others, wanting to arrive at the present time physically, or for variety, the spice of life. (See Chapter 11.)

GOOD STORY: A narrative vision of future benefit or advantage which is better than past or present circumstances and is worth working toward. Goals, dreams, expectations or what gives meaning to one's life.

HOLISTIC: A viewpoint that takes in the entire human being.

HOLISTIC ASPECTS: A division of the human being into four parts— mind, body, emotions and spirit—for the purpose of greater understanding of the functioning of the whole.

IDEAL: A pattern, model or goal of perfection.

INACCURATE ASSUMPTION: A belief or presupposition held as true, which is not true and which generates agitated energy by its interaction with absolute reality.

INDIVIDUAL: A particular, single and separate person.

KNOWING: Clear and certain understanding of information. Cognizance.

KINSHIP: Being in a family or family-like relationship.

LOVE: The benevolent feeling of nurturing energy from God for us, and through us to the rest of the world, including back to God.

MYSTERY: A condition of not knowing, not understanding or not having things explained; being in wonder.

MYSTICAL: Having some mysterious (transilient) meaning beyond human (transfixed) understanding.

NURTURING: Caring for, nourishing, taking care of, rearing.

ODYSSEY: A wandering journey with a long series of adventures.

OVERRUN: To go beyond or exceed the time and circumstances in which a particular assumption works best, into the time and circumstances when the opposite would work better and would heal the symptoms which have occurred.

POST-TRAUMATIC STRESS DISORDER: (PTSD) A symptomatic condition initiated by a severe traumatic event and followed by long term symptoms, such as hyperalertness, exaggerated startle response, irritability, anxiety, depression, insomnia, nightmares, flashbacks, difficulty focusing attention, poor memory, emotional numbness, explosive outbursts and headaches.

QUESTION-ANSWER PROCESS: The systematic steps (see Table I for the four steps) through which a person can ascertain and identify what is going on in the person's psyche ("mental computer"). The person both thinks up the issue to consider, and notices the response in inner experience. These steps are repeated in a sequence. At the end, the person can decide what to experimentally assume to be true in the immediate future.

REALITY: Actual existence; the true state of affairs; actual fact; truth; verity.

REINCARNATION: The belief that one's soul has lived before and will be reborn in the future, in other bodily form.

RELAXING: To become less stiff, tense, firm or fixed.

ROLE: The part assumed or function carried out by a person when participating in everyday life.

SAFETY: Freedom from harm or danger.

SELF: Whatever one considers one's own person to be at the moment.

SELF-AS-SOURCE: The keystone or beginning premise of Willowbrook Philosophy: The closest experience one can have of source in one's life is an experience of one's self.

SELF, BASIC: The ordinary experience of being one's own person when relaxed and not trying to be anything in particular.

SELF, DIVINE: The sacred, spiritual energy at the core of one's experience of being one's own person.

SELF, HIGHER: The person one could be if one were operating from a more complete degree of perfection as compared to one's everyday level.

SHATTERED GOOD STORY: A narrative vision of future benefit or advantage which is smashed by circumstances or events which prevent its fulfillment.

SOUL: An eternal aspect of self that thinks, feels and makes the body act, but does not include the body. Besides its spiritual aspect, it includes the personal, "mental computer" built in the present lifetime, plus highly charged assumptions brought over from previous incarnations.

SPACE-HOLDER: A person who provides and maintains a safe, calm, accepting atmosphere in which the Question-Answer Process can best be performed.

SPIRIT: The energetic aliveness of one's own person that influences the surrounding emotional atmosphere.

SPIRITUAL: Having to do with realms beyond the physical mechanistic world.

STRIVING: To try hard, work hard, endeavor; to struggle (with); to fight (against); to contend; to battle.

STRUCTURE OF (PERSONAL) REALITY: A personal belief system about truth including facts and evaluations.

TRANSILIENT: Spontaneously springing from one condition to another (in contrast to resilient which is springing back to original form).

TRANSILIENT ASSUMPTION: A statement which, when stipulated to be true, opens one to spontaneously arising inner experiences of unstructured freedom and energy.

TRANSILIENT GOOD: The benefit which spontaneously springs up in one's inner experience when one is open.

TRANSFIXED: Made motionless or firm by fastening, or pinioning.

TRANSFIXED ASSUMPTION: A statement which, when stipulated to be true, creates fixed structure in one's experience of reality.

TRANSFIXED GOOD: A benefit in the structured physical world.

TRANSFIXED GOOD STORY: A narrative vision of future benefit viewed in a context of time, including the past, present and future, in which the good imagined in the future is desired, worth working toward and gives a structured meaning to one's life. Synonymous with "a good story".

TRUE ASSUMPTION: The most accurate theory, belief, premise or supposition which is possible in the present circumstances. Accuracy is determined by the theory that works best, which in psychological issues is the one that is most calming of agitated energy, and most productive of nurturing energy.

TRUTH: **Fact**—A demonstratable physical reality.

Supposition—a theory or assumption which works best for the circumstances at hand.

Judgement—An operating (frequently spiritual) value (e.g. "The universe is good; God is good)

Affirmation—A suppositional truth that assumes a future good circumstance, not factually true at present, to be true. It is called "truth" because it works best in a situation that would otherwise produce burnout from excessive desire for the future good.

UNIQUE: Having no like or equal; being the only one of its kind.

UNIVERSE: The whole of existing things; includes a fundamental attribute of the spiritual realm in which one's assumptions interact with reality in an emotionally perceptible way, by generating calm if in alignment with reality, and agitation if not.

UNITY, THE: Oneness; the undivided whole as distinct from its parts.

WILLOWBROOK: A name for Dr. Allen's philosophy, as expressed in this book, chosen for the beauty of its sound and image.

A History of the Development of Willowbrook Philosophy

Origins

It was in high school that I first knew I wanted to be a psychiatrist. However, my early motivation was to understand the psyche, and from that knowledge to be able to cure mental problems. After graduating from Oberlin College as chemist in 1955, and while working in industry, I began to devour a wide range of journal articles and psychology books including the works of Jung. From the very beginning, I realized that the spiritual dimensions of humans play an essential role that can't be left out in a comprehensive understanding of the psyche. I found some spiritual elements in Jung, little in the other schools of psychology, and felt the inclusions even in Jung represented only bare rudiments.

After receiving my M.D. from Western Reserve University Medical School in Cleveland, Ohio, in 1961 I did my medical internship at Kaiser Permanente Hospital, San Francisco, in 1962. After two years as a medical researcher, I completed psychiatric residencies at Presbyterian Medical Center (University of Pacific) and the University of California, San Francisco, in 1967. I conducted a private practice in Menlo Park, California, for over 25 years. During that period the philosophy and methodology expressed in this book was developed and refined. The following sections describe the major elements, their roots and application.

Question-Answer Process

It became apparent very early in my career that a powerful tool was needed to harness the capacity of psyche to study itself. The tool that evolved, the Question-Answer Process, profoundly enabled the study of both the psychological and the spiritual aspects of mind. In terms of my own development, I was told I had shown a keenness with deductive logic as a high school student. However, I knew that logic alone was not sufficient to understand the mind. Over the years, I came to value the creative and intuitive process as equally important.

My initial realization in the development of the Question-Answer Process was that if a person could verbalize a question, they could intuitively perceive its answer arising in their inner experience. Next, was the observation that when one intuitively assumed the truth of inner answers, one could think through the subject area to obtain clarity. This stabilizing of the truth in Step 4 of the process, of what has emerged in Step 3, enabled the creatively derived material to have enough structure to be useful as an exploratory tool.

These realizations became the basis for the Question-Answer Process, the fundamental technique I used both personally and in my clinical practice. The beauty of the Q-A process is that it taps into people's own inner knowing, enabling them to take responsibility for their own answers. Unlike other forms of therapy, which impose an outer structure on the patient, the Q-A method frees the therapy to use whatever comes up.

Reincarnation

Being born and raised in Cleveland, Ohio, I was imbued with the prevailing Mid-Western idea that reincarnation was a strange belief held only by Far Eastern people. After I moved to California in 1961, it took me several years to become comfortable with the idea that reincarnation might be a useful paradigm. It seemed that a significant percentage of Californians already believed in it. In later years, as I became aware of techniques for processing people's memories of childhood experiences (such as in the Fischer-Hoffman Process which I discovered and experienced for myself in 1969), I naturally extended these techniques for processing memories of previous incarnations into my methodology. I found that the same general principles applied to past life memories as to childhood memories, if one expanded the idea of memories to include images of one's own prior death, after-death experiences, and conclusions drawn at such times.

Self-as-Source Principle

During the many years of my education, the general idea of the self-as-source principle had been one among a vast multitude of spiritual principles, many of which I felt were confusingly contradictory to each other. In 1973, I experienced the est Training. In the following six years I talked with other est graduate psychotherapists about the possibility of finding a principle that could be used to transform the practice of psychotherapy into one that included spiritual attributes in a useful way. In 1978, I settled on the idea of making the self-as-source principle, not just one among many, but the keystone and starting point of a new therapeutic context. The next step in the process—determining what attributes this self-that-is-source had—fit in with the est philosophy, where the attributes of self were called "concepts" (transfixing) and "experiencing" (transilient). Subsequent steps in the development of my theory expanded beyond the est framework, so I moved on at that point.

Complementary Contrary Pairs of Assumptions

Recalling the physicists' handling of their complementary contrary theories about the nature of light (the wave and particle models), I decided next to try dividing the self-that-is-source into four holistic aspects of mind, body, emotions, and spirit. I then identified a basic pair of complementary contrary beliefs about self (along the lines of the wave and particle theories) in each aspect. The result can be observed in Table III, which I saw in retrospect are amazingly similar to the original form from 1979. Another idea, that evolved, was that overrunning an assumption, using it past the time and circumstance in which it was appropriate, would result in a particular psycho-pathological condition. These conditions are listed in Table IV in their present form. Identifying these conditions proved the most difficult task, especially in the emotions aspect, and they have changed markedly from their original 1979 version. These changes followed as I evolved an understanding of the processes in healing these over-run conditions.

Transilient and Transfixing

In 1981, I was searching for accurate labels to apply to each side of the complementary contrary pairs of assumptions. On searching through the dictionary in the "trans-" section, while seeking a word that expressed "transformation", I came upon "transilient". It shares linguistic roots with "resilient" which means to spring back to original form. Transilient, on the other hand, means springing across or beyond, and had largely been used by botanists to refer to the phenomenon of seed pods spontaneously bursting and broadcasting their seeds. I liked this image immensely, and assigned the word, transilient, to the assumption which generated the opening, energizing, spontaneously arising experience. The opposite concept, the name to call the other side of the complementary contrary pair, seemed naturally to be "transfixing", defined as motionless and stationary, to refer to the structuring assumptions. These two terms proved both clear and useful over the years, and are still being used in same manner. I abbreviate them as TSL for transilient, and TSF for transfixing.

Willowbrook Philosophy

In 1982, I wanted to find a name for the whole philosophical context that was evolving. After a fruitless effort, I finally gave up trying to discover a name that meant something in particular and would be relevant to the theory. Instead, I elected to call it by a name that evoked a beautiful feeling. "Willowbrook" was my decision, and also became the name of the small educational foundation which I formed as a teaching vehicle, Willowbrook Foundation. Post-Traumatic Stress Disorder and Learned Helplessness was an example of a topic of an early Willowbrook symposium conducted in 1982, in which I applied early versions of my techniques.

Six Roles Balanced for Transilience and Transfixedness

Another development in 1982 was the recombination of the assumptions found in the four holistic aspects of self into distinct modes of personal functioning. It seemed appropriate to combine them in a way that included some transilient energy and some transfixed structure in each new mode, since a person would need some of each at all times. I decided to experiment with a 50:50 model, each version having half transilient assumptions and half transfixing ones. Mathematically, given four aspects, two in transilience and two in transfixedness, there were only six possible combinations.

I realized that these combinations could be viewed as roles that all of us act out in daily life. Each of the six have a different character. The character of each role is defined by the particular assumptions governing the role. The roles were given names which corresponded to a function for which their assumptions seemed especially appropriate. (See Table V.) The unique characteristics of each role were novel, but initially, the exact use of the roles was not clear. Gradually, over the years, several points became apparent.

First, a person did not assume one role and stick with it throughout life. Ideally, a person would shift into whichever role functioned best in their activity at the time.

Secondly, people seemed to gravitate toward and feel most at home in one of the three pairs of roles (their usual pair of roles). Each pair consisted of one role plus its opposite role in which all the assumptions were reversed. Whatever was transfixed in one became transilient in the opposite, and vice versa. The pairs are Roles 1 and 2, 3 and

4, 5 and 6. By functioning alternately in one usual role and then in its opposite, all the assumptions are exercised without shifting into any of the other four roles. However, what is missing in this way of functioning, is being able to use any of the other four roles comfortably when it is appropriate for the job at hand. (I felt a person could develop a spiritual exercise, which had as its goal being able to function with ease in any of the six roles.)

Thirdly, the nature of an ideal held by a culture could be identified and corrected. For instance, Western culture's ideal is to have a person operate in all four transfixed assumptions at once—a knowing, unique individual, striving for a particular good story (life myth). I soon realized that this ideal is not workable because it is excessively structured and does not allow for essential transilient energy.

On the other hand, Eastern cultures tend to idealize all four transilients all at once—a relaxed, empathic spirit experiencing the mystery of the eternal now. This is trying to live in nirvana all the time, which clearly lacks transfixed structure.

The fourth principle was discovered in 1991. It was then that I realized that the nature of God would appear in different ways, depending on which role a person was in at the time. Also, that the nature of God would appear to have the qualities of the opposite role of the pair. This discovery explained the different experiences of God which people described. The theory yielded six unique categories into which the various experiences of God seemed to fit. The six categories specified the assumptions to be made to generate each type of experience. (Table VII.) As an example of this theory's application, a spiritual seeker could choose to emphasize one way of experiencing God, or develop a daily routine for moving through each of the six experiences of God in turn.

Fractured Reality and Battered Reality Syndrome

By 1984, I had reached clarity about a heretofore unidentified syndrome. The syndrome resulted from trauma that was caused when the basic structure of a person's view of reality was wounded or "fractured" by the deliberate lies of a person close to them. The two Willowbrook symposia in 1984 focused on this "Battered Reality Syndrome" and the importance of telling the factual truth in all relationships. The symposia included emphasis on truth that had to be told about childhood sexual abuse and spousal abuse.

By 1984, such truth-telling had become more acceptable as compared to 92 years prior when Freud had been ostracized for attempting to tell the truth about his sexually abused patients to his colleagues. With my battered reality patients, co-detective work had to be done to identify the most likely "true facts." The patient had to effectively assume those facts to be true in spite of resistance, objections and denial from the close relative or friend who was lying. My patients and I were amazed by the speed with which healing occurred when the patient was able to assume the true facts in the traumatized family or work situations.

The Shattered Good Story

In 1985, the importance of a time-line from the past through the present, into the future, became apparent as the frame of reference of transfixed emotions (i.e. the valuing and desire for future good outcomes). The structured story or life myth in which one lives, including what one loves and desires for the future, was called a "good story" for short. It described that atmosphere, outcome, situation or result which was seen as better in the future as compared to what exists in the present or existed past. It was meaningful and viewed as worth working toward. When traumas occurred in the future, and the story did not work out as one had envisioned, a condition called a "Shattered Good Story" resulted. It was similar to the Battered Reality

Syndrome in that something structured (transfixed) was broken. What was broken was the view of factual reality in one case, and the myth or story about goals and the meaning of life in the other case. However, it was clear that, fundamentally, they were very different, because the process for healing the fractured reality by discovering, telling, and assuming the factual truth about the matter, did not heal a shattered good story. It would be another seven years of wrestling with the problem before I could state clearly in my principles what constituted the healing process for the shattered good story (See last section below).

Agitated Energy versus Nurturing Energy

In 1986, my attention moved to the muddled problem of psychic energy. By building on my observation that the very painful, agitated energy which occurred in the Battered Reality Syndrome, was immediately calmed by the person's assuming that which was factually true to be so, I decided to experiment with the idea of separating psychic energy into two basic categories, (bad) agitated energy and (good) nurturing energy. At first, agitated energy was confined to that experienced as *fear*, an emotion so clearly seen when a person is erroneously assuming a catastrophe is about to happen. In subsequent years, it became clear to me that in addition to fear, *sadness* and *anger* were also agitated energies being generated by inaccurate assumptions. I found that they could also be calmed by assuming a more accurate truth. After the calmness was attained, nurturing energies could then be generated by making more transilient assumptions (see list in Table III). The full extent of this principle's power, especially in the realm of the spirit, became apparent in subsequent years through a better understanding of transilient good.

New Primary Purpose To Know God and Glorify Him Forever

In 1987, in response to a serious health challenge, I decided to move beyond keeping my research methods rigorously scientific, and set out to explore spiritual realms by whatever means were available, including religious. After considerable meditation about it, a new life purpose for me evolved: "to know God and glorify him forever." I first encountered these ancient words in the Charles Williams novel, *War In Heaven*, which I had been reading and rereading for the previous twenty-five years. I then began searching for a spiritual tradition that was best for me in supporting this life purpose.

Self-as-source versus God-as-source

In 1989, I became a student of metaphysics in the Unity Church, a hundred year old tradition of practical, mystical Christianity. My first quandary was wondering how to reconcile Unity's principle of God-as-source with my own view of self-as-source. Within a year, I arrived at the following principle which for me answered this question:

I, myself, am source of the assumptions that create my personal view of reality, which includes the transilient assumptions that enable me to be open to experience the nurturing energies of the universe (love), of which God is the source.

Affirmations of Good (that are not factually true)

Given the extensive clinical evidence that assumptions of factual truth work best, I found Unity's affirmations of a good that was not factually true to be very disturbing within my theories at the time. The resolution became evident in 1991 when I realized that the function of affirmations was not some magical incantation to cause the envisioned good to come true. Rather, such affirmations enable a person, with their burning desire for a future good, to envision the good—and yet to be able to return to a calm feeling before burning out over the matter. Thus, the calming act (assuming to be true that which is not yet factually true) in the area of future good, values, and meaningfulness, proved to be the *exact opposite* of the act (assuming to be true that which is factually true) which produced calming in matters of factual truth. No wonder this problem had been muddled for so many years!

Up A Spiritual Creek Without Paddle

For many years, I struggled to find the right approach and voice for articulating these discoveries and philosophy to the world at large. The metaphorical title came to me first. The idea of basing the exposition on an allegory occurred while I was preparing for a seminar, in 1991, in which I presented the Willowbrook Philosophy and how it related to Unity's metaphysical principles. I began writing the book six months later.

Healing a Shattered Good Story

In 1992, the final piece of the puzzle fell into place. I made the last change in Table IV by moving a Shattered Good Story from the category of a transilient overrun in the emotions aspect of the self, to being a transfixed overrun there. Thus, it was in the opposite mode from a Battered Reality, which comes from overrunning the transilient assumption in the mind aspect of the self. Instead of the previously held notion, where one had to become more transfixed in order to heal the shattered good story in the emotions aspect, now one had to abandon it and return to the transilient state where a new good story would gradually develop.

In the mind aspect, the source of one's sense of reality was seen to be the ability to find out factual truth and assume it to be true, a transfixing process. By contrast, in the emotions aspect, the source of meaning in one's life was seen to lie in the ability to make the transilient assumption:

I exist in the present moment, the eternal now. I am just being aware of my experience now (including uplifting, spiritually nurturing experience) until a vision with meaning, a new good story about the future, spontaneously appears.

In the process of letting go of the old shattered good story, and allowing a new one to form, renewed meaning, direction, and enthusiasm result.

Looking Back

As I look back toward my original high school goal of understanding the psyche, it seems that I have, to a degree, succeeded. My intention was to scientifically figure out how the human psyche works. It started with using my own and my patients' minds as "laboratories." Using early versions of the Q-A process, I came up with assumptions, considered and tested them. The degree of workability was the criterion that kept me discarding, renewing and honing the assumptions. I encourage others who wish to build on this work to also learn to use the tools, make their new assumptions and test them in the laboratory of their minds and lives for workability. From this solid "reality" base, you can then build the spiritual assumptions and access the universal energies of joy and love.

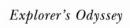

About The Author

Dr. Mary Allen, nee Mary Alice Hughes, was born December 26, 1932 in Cleveland, Ohio where she was raised. She received a B.A. in Chemistry (Phi Beta Kappa) from Oberlin College and an M.D. from Western Reserve Medical School (now Case Western Reserve). Her father, a renown Ph.D. scientist in organic chemistry, who was director of research for Standard Oil of Ohio (SOHIO/B.P.) for 35 years, is an atheist from a Protestant background. Her mother came from a Catholic family, was a speech educator and raised five children. Dr. Allen is the eldest of her siblings and all were brought up as vague Protestants.

She did her medical internship at Kaiser Hospital in San Francisco and psychiatric residency at Presbyterian Medical Center (now University of Pacific) and the University of California, San Francisco, and has resided Menlo Park, California, ever since. Dr. Allen has been a psychiatrist in private practice for twenty-five years and has served on the Community Physicians Staff of Stanford University Hospital during that period. She has been inspired by two psychiatrists who have combined the spiritual with the psychological in their work, M. Scott Peck and Elizabeth Kubler-Ross. Dr. Allen's favorite authors include a group of mystical Christian writers who called themselves The Inklings: Charles Williams, C. S. Lewis, and J.R.R. Tolkien.

She is married to an electronics industry executive who is Jewish, and they have two sons, both presently attending college. After raising her sons in Reform Judaism, in 1989 she joined Unity Church and became a student of its metaphysics.

My Poems from God

Mary Hughes Allen

The end is in the middle.
The last is always first.
There is no hoping without longing.
There is no loving without pain.
Give me your heart that I may break it,
And release the butterfly spirit within.
The spirit trapped in your heart
Is longing for return to the light.
Let it fly. It will do you no good trapped.
There is gold in the diamond if the sparkle dies.
Break your heart and let the liquid love
Turn your night into day, your lost into found.
Give me your broken heart
And I will show you the mysteries of a thousand worlds.

—5-26-91

There is no end.
All is in the now, only.

—5-26-91

There is nothing that is more than me.
All is clear.
Cleverly I have invented the baffles that obscure your
vision.
The sight of me is more than your hearts can bear.
Give me your love and your allegiance,
And I will manage this complex world for you.
There is naught else.
Come quietly and be mine.

—7-3-91

Quiet rocks. Quiet trees. Quiet water.
Quietly rooted in the depths of the earth,
Requiring no effort to exist in all their glory.
So you, too, believing you are heavily ladened,
Can be rooted in the center of your being,
And quietly just be.
You don't exist because you struggle and work hard.
You exist because the God center in you,
Lives you as you.
God is even more eternal than these rocks.
Live in God as God lives in you.
Let go of the day's worries,
And be quiet in eternity.
And when you want excitement instead of rest,
Think of the hard edges of the rocks,
Severe and unforgiving;
There is nothing woosy about their quietness.
Think of the tall trees,
Deep rooted,
Raising branches to sun, wind and rain
For centuries.
Think of the water lapping, slushing,
Whipped into waves by the wind.
They don't need your puny human efforts to have ex-
citement.

The most excitement you will ever have
Is to get in touch with the heart beat of the universe,
Tingling and glowing within your soul.
Give back to God all the circumstances in your life,
And trust that tomorrow,
He will return whatever you are to work on then.

—7-4-91

My child, be still and know that I am one.
I know every sparrow that falls.
Would I not know your every circumstance?
Give your all to me and we will dance
In the stars and play upon the waters.
All is well.
I have you in my heart.

—7-5-91

The wonder of it all
Collides
With the beauty of what has been.
In the mountains of your mind
Lie high alpine passes
Of rarefied air and cool pristine beauty.
There is much to learn with these mind mountains,
But remember always to come often to the valleys
With the homes and warm hearths of love,
Where you really live
And love
And have your being.

—8-7-91

Heroic comes from ancient lands,
The one whose noble mind and fiery spirit
Will give our mundane world
The hope and vision clear
To guide our way home,
Where we are missed and long past due.

—3-14-93

Brown bark darkly clothes the tree.
Strength flows up from roots toward blossoms.
The strength is the real tree,
More truly than bark or blossoms.
In the midst of strength,
In the middle of the trunk,
Lies the heart of the tree,
Pulsing and glowing,
Radiating light and love to all around.
The heart is not the tree.
The strength is the tree; the heart is me.
I love you that you may in turn
Love and live, and have your tree-like being.
Tune in to the beat.
Open your eyes to the radiance.
Join your heart with my heart,
And together we will create the world.

—4-24-93

A flame leaps high,
Showing the world by its light.
A camel's hump is high
Bearing the burdens of men.
A fish swims lowly,
In waters below the shore.
The Son of Man comes softly,
So as not to disturb

The natural order of things.
Softly, softly, gently tending the lambs.
No thought for the morrow has he,
But only gentle love in the present.
Give your hearts, oh humans,
To the Son of God who comes gently.
Let your love for him
Overflow in the bountiful harvests of the world.
Give your love to him
And never hold back.
There is naught else that you know
That is worth teaching.
There is naught else that you know
That is worth living.
Be gentle in your loving the Son of Man.
No more crucifixions.
No more miraculous disruptions
Of the natural order of the world.
Only natural gentle steps to be taken
To lead to the promised land,
Where good stories will shatter and die,
Just as they always have.
But now the heart of mankind
Will yield and let itself be broken,
Willingly,
Without losing consciousness
Of its ground of being.
Rooted in the Most High,
Identifying with its eternal nature,
The God in us
Will be known and glorified.

—4-26-93

You are not alone.
You are never alone.
All your life
You have had with you
The guardian angels of all times.
Give your light to them
That they may shine and illuminate your path.
Give them your loving gratitude,
That they may in turn shower love upon you.
Flow with their radiant energy,
That they may affectionately eddy around you.
Give them your time.
Instruct them in your ways,
That they may be more effective in your world.
Love with them in your house,
That you may feel the comforting warmth of their presence.
You are truly never alone.
What you are experiencing
When you feel the empty loneliness,
Is only the hollow place closing you off,
Built by your own assumptions
That deny the reality of my angels.
Dissolve the barriers you have erected.
Such barriers are only for emergency situations,
Where you have strayed amongst evil people.
There the barriers are essential to defend you,
Until you have time to distance from the evil,
And choose another path.
Once safe, you have to remember
To dissolve the barriers again.
You are not alone.
Never have you been alone,
Even if you felt you were.
Touch the hem of my garment
And let my love pour into you.
These are your roots to life.
These are your connections to the Kingdom
The vibrant glowing essence within you.

My power and energy will shake your roots.
Your job is to find the renewed truth
That will calm the shaking.
When the energy is smooth
As molten glowing glass,
I will come to you in all my glory
And my Kingdom will be yours.

—4-27-93

Your heart is filled with pain and sadness.
It drips with bitter water that cannot give life.
Go deep within you, right to the core.
Find there a tiny spark of light.
This spark is hardy and self-sustaining,
Even in the midst of the bitter water.
This spark will always be there.
It will sustain your life forever.
But you do not want to rely on it
Because its edges are harsh with truth.
Let its sharp edges cut away
The rotten parts of your heart.
Let the truth slice through the bitterness,
Scraping away the pain and sadness,
Until you have laid bare
Your living heart, pulsating with life.
You will never miss the pain and sadness;
Let them go with the bitter water.
When you touch them in the future,
Let them only be as a warning signal
That something needs cutting away
By the hard edges of truth.
Your heart will then bleed fresh blood and life,
Showering them upon your world
Like the sweet water of rain
That brings plants to life in the spring.
The growing plants will then nurture you, in turn,
And life will be good.

Shy not away from the sharp edges of the light of truth.
They will cleanse your life so you can function
As I mean you to do,
With joy and radiance,
Enlivening a thousand worlds.

—5-1-93

My child! My child!
How I despair to see you in such agony.
Give yourself to me.
Let go of all the worldly things
That you have clung to in your responsibility.
Give over to me the out working of all things.
Pass it over like a football.
Let it go and give no thought of tomorrow.
Today, I have you well in hand and supported.
Tomorrow does not yet exist.
I am in process of creating it,
And even I do not know with certainty
How it will turn out.
Be centered with me in the now.
Be nurtured by the energies
Which I command in the present.
I send my energies of love to you.
Feel them and enjoy.
Revel in your good fortune.
Dance in your ecstasy.
Move yourself in the dance,
And feel my love.
What else could you desire
That would be more wonderful than this?
Whatever it is, I will give you that, too,
In this eternal now moment.
Tomorrow your goals for the future
Will show up in the world,
Visible for you to see and desire.
You will see them with big flags and signs

Attracting your attention.
There are plenty of goals,
And you will be aware of them and desire them
Without thinking of them now.
Now fill your batteries
With the radiant energies of the universe,
Yours for the taking,
From the beginning of time.

—5-2-93

Today I am angry, you Little Ones!
Today I am full of wrath and rage.
How dare you stand on your firm ground,
And shout to everyone that you have life all together.
How dare you boast that you are in charge and com-
mand.
Will not your firm ground be rent with earthquakes?
Will it not be worn by flood waters?
Will it not have trees and rocks fall on it in wind storms?
You puny humans!
Get out of my sight with your audacity.
Hide your arrogant selves from my view.
I, your God, created you,
And I will uncreate you when the times comes.
Your idiocy is more than I can take today.
I ask myself what assumption
Is generating my anger today.
The answer is that I expected you to understand.
I created you so that you would know me,
And be a glory to my eyes forever.
I gave you the situation on earth,
And caused you to be born into it.
The system will work
If you live in the truth of its ways.
The system will work to know me,
And glorify me forever.
But the system will not work

To give you the power
To have all your good stories come true forever.
You have mistaken my intention in making the world.
It is true that you need goals and visions of future good.
You need them just as you need air,
As long as you have a human body.
But it was not my intention
That all your visions of future good
Should come to pass without mishap.
That would make you a rigid machine,
Churning out visions of good,
And mechanistically manifesting them.
I did not create you to be machines.
I created you to be lovers,
And lovers have their hearts broken,
Periodically and repeatedly,
All in the midst of their great joy
And longing for their beloved-of-the-moment.
Face the truth of it.
I meant for your hearts to experience
Both the heights of passion
And the depths of despair.
This will always be.
Do not have an ideal of ending
The possibility of episodes of despair,
Anymore than ending the possibility of joy.
The correct ideal, you blind fools,
Is to live with me in your hearts,
In the present moment, in the eternal now.
You are higher and more real
Than all the longings and despair of your everyday
world.
Learn, my children, what I have created you for,
And rest all of your days
In the hand of my love.

—5-3-93

I give to you, Oh my children,
Of life everlasting.
I love you,
And I want you to prosper.
How can I explain to you,
In words you can understand,
The system I have created for you?
The system will work well,
If you understand it,
And use it wisely.
It will *not* work, however,
To achieve the excessively transfixed ideals
That you have at present.
How can I change your stubbornness?
How can I get your attention?
Sit down and listen to my heart.
Make it your heart,
And all will be well.
Note that from my heart
I pour forth loving enlivening energy
To everything in your world.
I cause its existence,
Not in the past like a clock set running,
But in the present.
I cause it in every moment of your lives.
I cause, please note,
The events of both your joys and your sorrows.
But I don't cause your pain deliberately.
I cause it in passing,
As I pour forth my love to everything.
I gave you humans the power
To dance in the world,
Among my creations.
I gave you the power
To pour forth your own love,
Even as I do.
But in order to do that,
To create you existing in the world,
I also had to give you the ability

To create a stable structured view of reality
In your personal lives.
If you did not have this ability,
You would float and be carried
Wherever the winds of life blew you.
You would have no authority,
And be creating no dance steps of your own.
You had to be given this ability
To take authority, to take dominion,
Though even in doing that,
I had to give you free will
To take dominion or not.
However, you have overstepped your bounds.
You have taken dominion
Where I meant you to leave it to me.
I cannot prevent you from doing it.
I gave you free will to create
The dance steps of your life.
It would not work for you to be my children
If you did not have this power.
The only way I can indicate to you
That I did not mean for you
To extend your dominion to the energies of love,
Is to have created it
So that it won't work if you do it.
Thus I created pain and sorrow,
And all agitated energies
To give you a warning sign
That you were doing something wrong.
I created pain to get your attention
To something you needed to correct,
Not to punish you,
And not because I made a mistake
That I need to correct.
Please understand!
I gave you the power to take dominion
Over your dancing, and
Over your choosing your own vision of future good,
But I reserved to myself

The power of the energies
That pour forth to manifest the future.
I do it from my heart of absolute good,
And therefore all things
Are good in my eyes.
However, they often do not
Correspond to the good you envisioned.
It is your job to stay centered and balanced
In my heart, the source of these energies,
Don't center yourselves
In your visions of good in the future.
Only visualize them.
Then let go of the ones that do not come true,
While rejoicing in the ones that do.
Let neither the rejoicing nor the letting go
Take precedence over your allegiance
To my heart.
Both joy and pain are play things
Compared to the majesty and power
Of my love.
Be with me always in paradise,
And you will also have
The best of all possible things
With which to play.

     —5-4-93

Harken all ye who are in error.
Correct your ways.
Do so today,
For tomorrow never comes in these matters.
Show yourselves to be men and women of truth.
Be accurate and precise
In all your dealings.
Correct your assumptions
Until you are both calm and happy.
Choose what to put your attention on,
And then love it with all your heart and soul.

Give nurturing to it and let it flourish.
Let not the mysteriousness of my presence
Deter you from being centered
Always in my heart.
Rest in my love,
And be a willing participant and conduit
Of my loving energies
As they pour out into the world.
Don't give up hope for the future,
But neither should you count on it
To give your life meaning.
You will find all the meaning you need,
Right now, right here, in my heart.

—5-5-93

There once lived, in the land of Canaan,
A woman who did her daily duties.
She carried the water in a jar on her head.
She cooked with olive oil in her kitchen.
She tended her family well.
But she felt that there was something more.
There was something missing in her life.
She felt an emptiness which she longed to fill.
She went to seek the thing that would fill it.
First she went to the village's holy buildings.
Then she went into the beautiful countryside.
She sought for it in the eyes of her loved ones,
And she prayed for it in the nights when she lay awake.
What is it that I am missing? she asked.
Ask not what, but who, came the answer.
Who are you? she wondered.
I am that I am;
I am who you are missing, came the response.
How do I fill my empty space with you? she asked.
I give myself to you,
With all my radiant loving energy, came the reply.
You may be giving,

But I have to prepare the receiving, she said.
She went further in her search,
Seeking how to receive.
Again she went into the world,
Asking wise holy men.
She went walking in the quiet buzz of the woods.
She examined how she received love from her family.
She looked and looked to find clues
About how to receive the radiant loving being.
Nowhere did she find her answer.
Nothing she could think of seemed to work.
Finally, in desperation, she asked her donkey:
What can a dumb animal like you teach me? she que-
ried.
I can teach you humility, the donkey seemed to answer.
I can teach you submission to the lash,
And openness to the fond caress,
But I can never teach you
The way that works with the higher order of things.
She sat down beside the donkey,
And wept in her despair.
Then she mused to herself:
Since there is no one else to teach me,
I have only myself left to rely on.
I know that within myself
I can assume I am that I am,
And be the unity of all.
I know that I can experience myself
Dividing into me and God.
I can see myself taking the path of being human,
Making assumptions to structure my reality,
And being aware of experiences as they arise within me.
I can see God taking the path of being
The radiant enlivening energy of love in the universe.
I can see that where I bog down
Is in the relationship between me and God.
I am reluctant to love
All the enlivening things God sends me.
The crushing defeats and tortuous pain

Are more than I can encompass.
God speaks to me and tells me to come up higher.
To be, in perspective, above the pain and failures.
Then I ask God: Why did you send me out
To experience the pain and failures in the first place?
I didn't, replies God. You did.
You went of your own choosing and volition.
You went seeking life and experience,
And you were free to experiment.
When you became totally bogged down and stuck
In the pain and failure,
Did you expect me to leave you there?
If I sent more enlivening loving energy,
It only increased your experience of pain and failure.
How was I to rescue you?
The only way I knew
Was to send you the emptiness,
The oblivion of non-awareness.
I hoped that eventually
You would become healed enough
To be aware of the emptiness,
And seek to fill it again.
This time I hoped you would have
More understanding of the system,
So you could fill it with love and joy,
Rather than pain and failure.
You have the choice.
Let go of the pain and failure
Of your shattered dreams,
And live within the warm love
Of my radiant heart
All the days of your life.

—5-8-93

My radiant sacred heart
Abides in you always.
Love it, give to it time and attention.
Lie down with it, and rise up with it.

Sleep with it, and
Take it with you in all your daily activities.
Hold it sacred.
Never let it go.
See your goals and visions of future good
Through the radiance of my sacred heart.
Always keep my heart as a glass seen through,
The ground of being from which you live.
My heart is the generating image,
Not the good you see and desire in the future.
Your desire is generated by my heart.
Without it as the source and roots,
The tree of your desire will burnout, wither and die.
Your desires are only like a compass needle,
Giving your life direction.
Without my heart, you lack the energy to move any-
where.
In my heart I know your real desires.
When you say, "I desire this good thing to eat",
You really mean "I desire a pleasant experience".
That pleasantness I will give you,
Even though it comes without your favorite food.
Come live with me in my radiant heart.
Love what I love,
And be loved in turn.
Your life will shine as a beacon
To others lost on the path,
And you will glow with the radiance of love.

—5-10-93

All is cold and frozen.
No signs of life move on the land.
In the heavens, the moon is cold,
And the clouds cover the sun by day.
Here, in a land with almost no signs of life,
One red flower exists.
It has blossomed from roots wedged in stones.
It has prevailed when blown by the winds.

Its petals are delicate but tough,
And do not tear or wither in the storms.
This one flower exists
Through the whole eternity of cold and darkness.
This one flower with its golden center of stamens.
This one flower of beauty and life
Persists and lives in these barren conditions.
I give you this one flower,
So that you will not forget.
I give you the flower to remind you,
And the pains and agitations to warn you.
I did not leave you without guidance.
The pathway is marked.
Follow the trail of red flowers
As they appear in your life.
Correct the erroneous assumptions
Which are generating the pain and agitation.
Give yourself, on your journey,
At least these guiding signs,
And know that you are not alone.
Even if it turns out that all of your life
The cold and darkness persist—
Even if there is no hint
That warmth and light will ever prevail—
These guides are enough.
When you see the red glow
Of the flower of my love,
Do not turn cynically away.
When you feel the firm guidance
I have left you,
Of pain and agitation to warn you
To correct your inaccurate assumptions,
Do not become angry at the signs.
I have left you enough guidance to follow,
To lead you on the narrow path
Through the barren land.
On this path you will be safe
From falling into pits of greater error and torment.
On this path you will keep your selfhood,

Your awareness, and your ability to function.
Thus, on that miraculous day
When the sun shines again,
Life comes to the land,
And love prevails,
You will be able to step into it joyfully.
You will not need eons of time
For finding your way back from the pits.
This is your path.
I have left the markers.
It is your choice whether you follow them.
My wish is for you to follow
The trail of the red flowers of my love,
Staying calm in the middle of the way,
So that I may greet you promptly
With my radiant loving self
On the day that the sun breaks through.

—5-11-93

Fear not, as I have told you before.
You are now clear on how to calm your fear.
You have only to seek your belief
Which is generating the fear,
Find a calming belief,
And assume it to be true instead.
So why are you not doing it?
I said to fear not, and I meant it.
Do you think you are doing it right
To honor and retain these fears,
Running your mental fingers
Through the agitated feelings,
Over and over again?
Hear me well! This is not doing it right!
You decided that honoring your fears
Was the right thing to do
When evil perpetrators lied to you,
And told you to be afraid of them,

In order for them to gain control over you.
I do not seek to control you with fear.
I only gave you the fearful agitation
To warn you that you have
An inaccurate belief that needs correcting.
I am not controlling you
To keep you on the narrow path.
I made the path to give you calm,
As you travel through the maze of life.
I made the fearful agitation
So that you could determine
The location of the calm path,
To give it a boundary you could sense.
Wicked people have used the fear I gave you
To enslave you.
I did not do this,
Though I gave them the free will
To be able to do it.
I gave the rest of you
The possibility of understanding
My system of fear as warning boundaries,
So you could use them appropriately.
I did not give you fear to let you be manipulated
By the lying perpetrators among you.
You are all created free,
And have the tools to stay free,
And be calm on the narrow path of truth.
Break the chains of those who would terrify you.
They have no power over you,
If you choose the calm of truth.
If they threaten to kill you,
You can remember that in death
You are safe in my home.
If they threaten you with pain,
You can remember that in pain
You can dissociate and leave your body.
No one is required to stay in pain
In order to manifest good in the world.
You may choose to endure

Such pains as of childbirth
In order to manifest the good
Of the having the child be alive in the world.
This is your choice,
And a noble one if you choose it.
But useless pain is not noble.
How can you judge if a pain is useless?
Ask yourself whether it is useful
For manifesting a good thing in the world,
Which I have not found another way
To manifest without pain.
You will know.
Once you know, honor your knowing.
Throw off the chains
Of useless pain and fear.
Follow the path of calm
Which I have laid out for you
Since the beginning of time.
I will create the future,
As you follow this path,
In the best possible way for all concerned.
This is your best chance
For the happy, harmonious life you desire.
Pay attention only to truth,
And the signs that you have strayed from the path,
Knowing you need to correct your assumptions.
Stay calm in my heart,
And my joy will be yours forever.

—5-12-93

My child, lean closer,
That you may hear me.
Focus your attention
That you may know my words.
Until now you have lived your lives
As if you were beasts running
From that which beat you
And frightened you.

I have told you that you are not to fear.
Each of you ask your own selves
What assumption you believe
Which is generating this fear.
Each of you will find your own answer.
Each of you has the choice
To change to a calming belief.
Each of your calming beliefs
Will be unique and different.
Each of you will know in your heart
What belief would calm you.
Each of you has the choice
To stay in fear and run with the mob,
Or to change to the calming belief.
Then you will have enough peace
To be able to hear me,
And to receive my love.
There is no way to force a choice for calm.
All force simply adds to the fear.
Education about the fact
That everyone has the choice
Is the only intervention
That has a chance of working.
Let your lives be lived
In the calm atmosphere of my love.
Let others who choose fear
Be distant from you who choose calm.
Then you will not be agitated
By their fear or their running.
Give yourself pause,
In the busy days of your activities,
And remember my calm.
Remember that I love you.
Then life will be as good as it can be,
Forever and ever.
Let my love for you
Inspire you with love
For everyone and everything
Upon which your attention focuses.

Let this inspiration be the energy
That fuels your lives.
Run not from fear,
But toward what you love,
And your lives will have joy everlasting.

—5-21-93

Receive. Receive.
My love comes to you
As waters flow down a waterfall.
There is naught else for you to seek.
Be calmed and soothed
By the waters of my love.
There is nothing else which has
The authority to command your attention.
Those nagging, flitting thoughts
Of your day-to-day life
Are like gnats buzzing in your mind.
They can be annoying,
If you pay attention to them.
They are not important.
Focus your attention on my love.
Your mind will throw up a warning,
Saying that it is not practical
To ignore your buzzing busy thoughts.
But I say to you:
If what you want is peace and well-being,
Paying attention to your thoughts
Is not practical.
It will not enable you to attain your goal.
Give me your attention.
Focus on whatever experience of my love
Is occurring to you at the moment.
See the radiance of my sacred heart
Pouring forth wonderful energy
Into your inner experience.
See the budding branches and blossoms of spring,
Full of the life force,

And bursting forth in vibrant joy.
Let the love from your family
Show you the warm comforts of home.
See the eagle soaring on high,
Just as your thoughts rise in your mind
With spiritual knowledge
And untold possibilities.
See a baby look up at you
With trust and yearning for your nurturing.
See the days of the world unfolding,
Traveling the path of time
On which cultures have flourished and died,
All in the light of the sun.
All these things are manifesting my love for you.
These are the forces of good in your life.
Focus your attention on them,
And receive the bounty which I want to give.

—5-24-93

Once there was a people,
Strong and fair,
Who sought to challenge
The gods in their power.
They rode forth in their chariots.
With a firm hand, they strove
To maintain peace in the world.
It was inevitable that their attempt should crumble.
There was nothing they could have done
To make it come out right.
Given their challenging, strong-arm attitude
They could create nothing
Of lasting peace in the world.
Yet neither could their fellow men
Across the river.
They had the opposite attitude.
They were so gentle and passive
That they were quickly over-powered
By any passing perpetrators.

Their attempt died just as quickly.
Both groups saw the source
Of the power for good in themselves
Instead of in me.
There is a power of which you are the source.
You have the power
To make assumptions about truth.
If you do not assume dominion
Over your own assumptions,
There is no hope for you.
You will never be functional enough
To join me in creating your good.
Truth and goodness are different and separate,
And always will be.
So let me tell you,
You creatures who are
The source of your own assumptions,
How to join with me in creating your good:
First, stand tall and strong.
Feel yourself alive and capable,
Free in your choices of assumptions,
And clear in your vision of what is true.
Now stand beside me.
See me as a glowing radiant being
With the power to create good.
It pours forth from my hand in streams of energy.
Where my enlivening hand
Touches a branch,
Leaves grow and blossoms spring forth
In a blaze of new life.
Where my hand touches a human soul,
Love is ignited
And flames forth from the heart.
Such a person is suddenly transformed
Into a person of zeal and passion.
But unless the person stays grounded in truth,
The passion only produces
More misery in the world.
The annals of history are full of examples

Of passionate men, who were sure they were right,
Yet created atrocities beyond imagination.
So how do you stay grounded in truth,
When the fiery energy of my hand
Touches your soul?
There is only one way:
You have to stand tall,
And remember what kind of a being you are.
This being is really above the passion,
And senior to it.
This being is in charge of the assumptions
That build strong conduits of truth
Through which the passion can flow.
Just as river beds and irrigation pipes
Direct and guide the flow of water,
So must your assumptions
Direct and guide the passion of my energy.
Do not be seduced
By the blinding rapture of my glory,
Thinking that it knows what it is doing.
Do not seek for guidance about what is good,
Or what is meant to be,
From the raw magnificence
Of my radiant being.
Bask in its glory.
Be enlivened by its vibrancy.
But never forget who you are:
You are far more important
Than all the glory in the universe.
You, who think of yourself as nothing much,
Are, in fact, agents of creation.
Ask yourselves "What do I want?"
Envision it,
And create assumptions that produce it.
If your old assumptions don't work
To produce your vision,
Experiment with new ones.
There is no one else who can do it.
I cannot do it.

Everything I touch is imbued with passion.
Only you can structure the world,
Deciding which leaves will grow,
And what type of flower will bloom.
That guidance is created by you,
Or has been created by you in the past,
Whether you remember doing it or not.
Structuring the DNA to genetically
Manifest your vision was your act.
Structuring the nature
Of your future good is your choice.
Don't forget who you are.
Take dominion over truth.
Then join with me to receive
The blessing of energy and passion.
Together we will create paradise on earth.

—5-25-93

Child, things are hard and heavy.
Do not lose heart.
Stay in your center and rest.
Let the energies around you be calm.
Hold the love you feel for others
In the palm of your hand.
Let its glow radiate
Into all the world.
There is nothing more important
To do than this glowing
That gives a light to the world.
Find your own comfort
And nurturing support
By moving about in my presence
Until you feel the warmth of my love.
Then be still and
Know that I love you.
Stand tall in your door way,
And on the top of your highest hill.
Stand and look out at the world.

See with clear vision
The truth of your land.
Then, travel in search
Of the light in your land.
Seek the shimmers and sparks
That give you clues about its location.
Go to the places of light in your land,
And offer your love and support
To those around who are tending it.
The light will grow
Until it becomes as bright as dawn,
Enabling you and the others
To see the truth of what is so in the land.
Without the light
The truth exists
But is not visible.
Without the truth, how can you know
Where to focus my love
Which comes through you
To manifest the glorious good in the world?
Seek the light
That enables you to see the truth.
Open to the experience of my love
That you may be
A radiant source of love in the land.
Without either one—truth or love —
Your life will not work.
Without the light of truth,
The fiery passion of love
Will either go to waste in a desert,
Or inappropriately burn and wound everyone.
Without the heat of love,
The light of truth is cold and barren,
Showing what is so,
But having no energy to bring anything to life.
Follow in the footsteps of your ancestors
Who both sought truth and felt love.
You can know they did this,
Because if they had not done so

You would not be here now.
Do not try to see
The particular circumstances of the future.
The future is not yet decided.
Let it unfold
In the mystery and great complexity
Of life in the world.
In regard to the future,
See only the particular good of the next step.
Hold it lightly,
As even the next step
May turn out differently
From your vision of it.
See the next step
In its vision of goodness,
But be ready to let go of the vision
As the truth of reality unfolds.
It is your responsibility
To see the next step.
Only you have the vantage point
To perceive what might be good for you.
But you do not have the perspective
To be able to see the highest good for all concerned.
That is my job.
Both of our viewpoints are necessary
To unfold the good in the world.
Just because your future good
Does not turn out the way you envisioned it,
Do not think that you did your job wrong.
Your envisioning the future good
Is essential to the process.
Just be willing to let it go
And find the good in what actually happens,
So the pain of your broken heart
Is not more than you can bear.
Follow in these ways,
And all will be well.

—5-26-93